NOW THAT'S WHAT I CALL MUSIC! 95

Wise Publications
part of The Music Sales Group
London/New York/Paris/Sydney/Copenhagen/
Berlin/Madrid/Hong Kong/Tokyo

Published by:
Wise Publications
14-15 Berners Street, London,
W1T 3LJ, UK.

Exclusive Distributors:
Music Sales Limited
Distribution Centre, Newmarket Road,
Bury St Edmunds, Suffolk, IP33 3YB, UK.

Music Sales Pty Limited
4th floor, Lisgar House, 30-32 Carrington Street,
Sydney, NSW 2000, Australia.

Order No. AM1012572
ISBN: 978-1-78558-456-5

Edited by Naomi Cook & Louise Unsworth.
Guitar chords edited by James Welland.

Printed in the EU.

Your guarantee of quality:
As publishers, we strive to produce every book
to the highest commercial standards.

This book has been carefully designed to minimise awkward page turns and to make playing from it a real pleasure.

Particular care has been given to specifying acid-free, neutral-sized paper made from pulps which have not been elemental chlorine bleached. This pulp is from farmed sustainable forests and was produced with special regard for the environment.

Throughout, the printing and binding have been planned to ensure a sturdy, attractive publication which should give years of enjoyment.

If your copy fails to meet our high standards, please inform us and we will gladly replace it.

www.musicsales.com

Ain't Giving Up

Words & Music by Craig David & Bruce Fielder

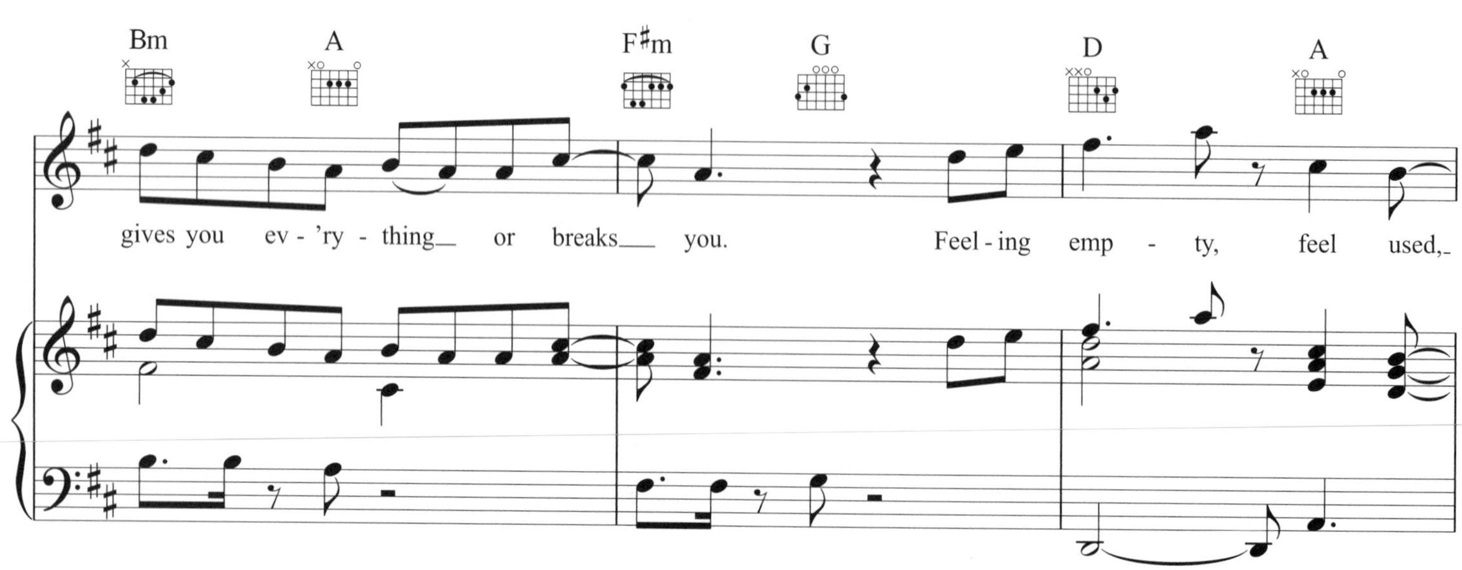

G A D A G A D A
it's like we're run - ning off fumes, a lit - tle bro - ken, con -
G A Em F♯m G A
- fused, but one thing I know for sure: ain't giv - ing up on you,
Bm F♯m G A Bm F♯m G
ain't giv - ing up on you,
A Bm F♯m G F♯m
ain't giv - ing up on you, ain't giv - ing up on you,

Em
F♯m
G
A
Bm
F♯m7
ain't giv - ing up on you. Oh, oh, oh,
G
A
Bm
F♯m7
G
A
ain't giv - ing up on you. Oh, oh, oh, ain't giv - ing up on
Bm
F♯m7
G
A
Em
F♯m
you. Oh, oh, oh, ain't giv - ing up on you,
G
A
Bm
F♯m7
G
A
ain't giv - ing up on you.

Bm
F♯m7
G
A
Bm
F♯m7
To Coda ⊕
G
A
Em
F♯m
G
A
Ain't giv - ing up on you.
When the
N.C.
go - ing gets tough
just re - mem-ber it's me and you
for life and when the world is not e - nough,
ba - by, are we

Bm7
F♯m7
worth the fight?
Feel-ing emp - ty, feel used,
G
Bm7
F♯m7
G
it's like we're run - ning off fumes.
A lit - tle
Bm7
F♯m7
G
Em
F♯m
bro - ken, con - fused
but one thing I know for sure:
D.S. al Coda
Coda
G
A
G
A
ain't giv-ing up on you.

Ain't My Fault

Words & Music by Uzoechi Emenike, Zara Larsson & Mack

Bm
ain't my fault__ you keep turn - ing me on. It ain't my fault__ you got,
(2.) ain't my fault__ you came here look - ing like that, you just made me trip,__ fall, and
got me so gone. It ain't my fault__ I'm not leav - ing a - lone. It
land on your lap. Cer - tain bad boy smooth, bo - dy hot - ter than the sun. I don't
ain't my fault____ you keep turn - ing me on. I can't
mean to be rude____ but I look so damn good on ya. Ain't got
talk right now, I'm look-ing and I like what I'm see-ing, got me feel-ing kind - a shocked right now. Could-a
time right now, miss me with that 'What's your name? Your sign?' right now. It's

stopped right now, e - ven if I want-ed, got - ta get it, get it, get it while it's hot right now.
light out - side, I just called an U - ber and it's right out - side.
Oh my god, what is this? Want you all in my bus-'ness, ba-by, I in - sist. Please don't blame me
G
Bm
for what - ev - er hap-pens next. No, I can't be re - spon - si - ble
F♯m
G
if I get you in trou - ble now. See you're
f

Bm
A/C♯
D
F♯m
too ir - re - sis - ti - ble,
yeah, that's for sure.
So if I
G
Bm
F♯m
put your_ hands_ where my eyes__ can't see,
then you're the__ one__ who's got a
G
Bm
A/C♯
D
hold__ on me.
No, I________
can't be re - spon - si - ble,
F♯m
F♯
Bm
re - spon - si - ble,
it ain't my fault.
No,
no,
mf

no, no, no, no, no, it ain't my fault.
To Coda
No, no, no, no, no, no,
1.
2.
Em7
F♯m7
no, it ain't my fault. 2. It
it ain't my fault.
Ba - by, one, two,
f
Gmaj7
Em7
F♯m7
Gmaj7
three, your bo - dy's call - ing me and I know wher - ev -

B♭maj7
D/A
-er is ex - act - ly where I wan - na be but don't blame
Gm/B♭
N.C.
me, it ain't my fault, it ain't my fault.
mf
No, no, no, it ain't my fault. No, no,
D.S. al Coda
oh my, oh my, oh my, oh my. So if I

Coda

it ain't my fault. It ain't my fault you got me so caught. It
It ain't my fault.

ain't my fault you got me so caught.
It ain't my fault.

It ain't my fault, well, that's too bad, it ain't my fault.

Alarm

Words & Music by Wayne Hector, Steve Mac, Ina Wroldsen, Anne-Marie Nicholson & Marshmello

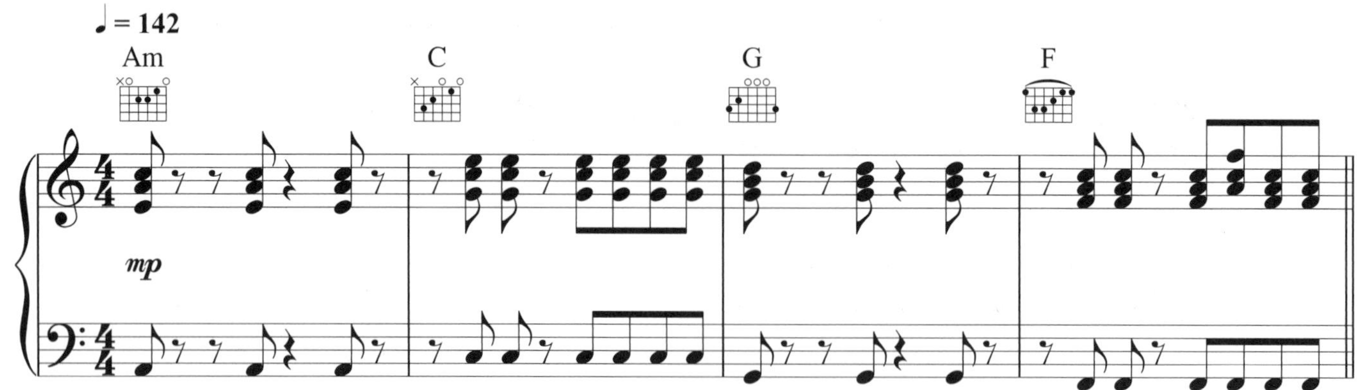

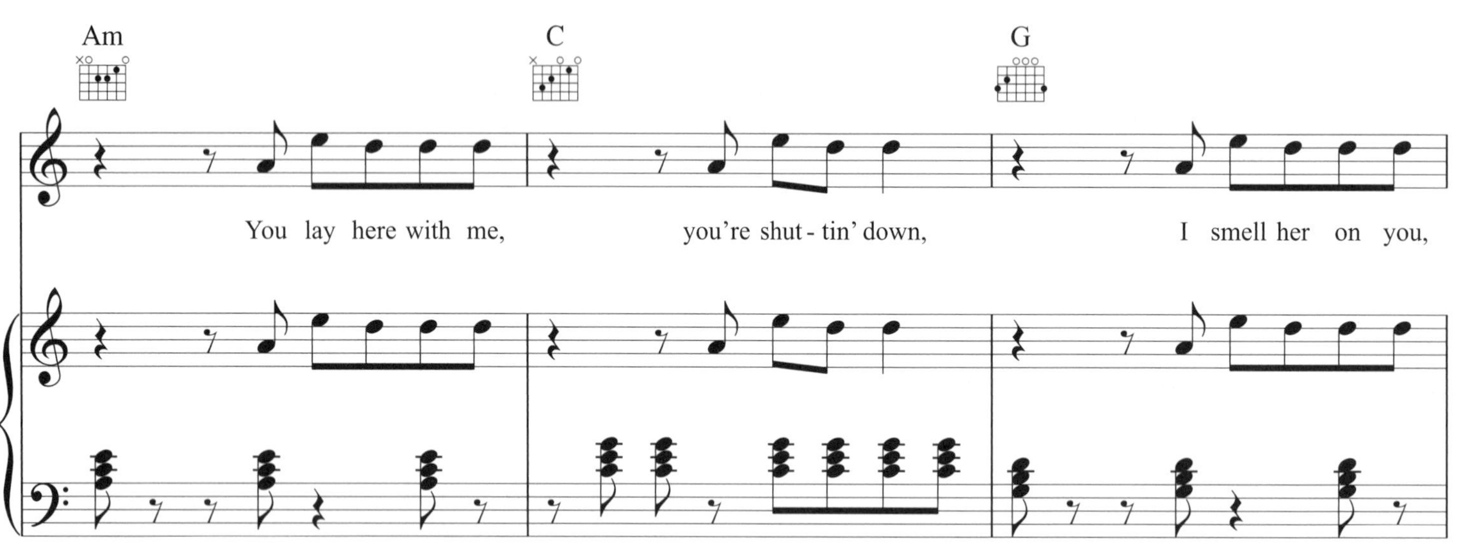

G
F
Am
I know what's hap-pened here__ in our bed, yeah.
Your phone is buz-zin',
C
G
F
so pick it up,
I know she call-in',
so what the ****?
Am
C
G
I should-'ve known a cheat stays a cheat-er,
so here we are.__
Am
C
And there goes the a-larm,
ring-in' in my head like some-bo-dy
f

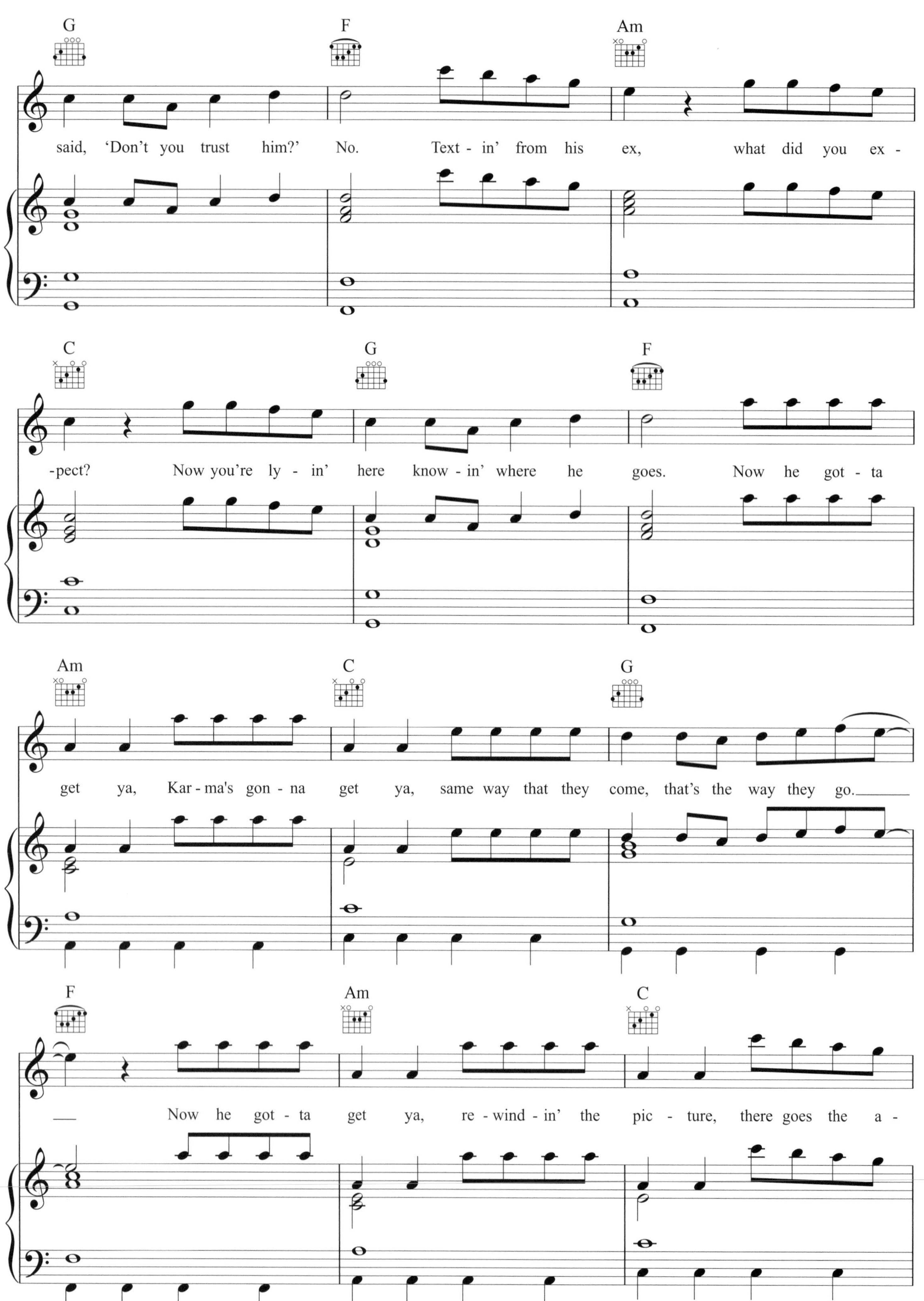

G F Am
said, 'Don't you trust him?' No. Text - in' from his ex, what did you ex -
C G F
-pect? Now you're ly - in' here know - in' where he goes. Now he got - ta
Am C G
get ya, Kar - ma's gon - na get ya, same way that they come, that's the way they go.
F Am C
Now he got - ta get ya, re - wind - in' the pic - ture, there goes the a -

G
-larm and the si - ren's go, there goes the a -
Am C G F
-larm. I saw it com - in', I let it go, my girls will tell me,
mf
Am C
'I told you so.' But I was so in - trigued by your style, boy,
G F Am C
al - ways been a suck - er for a wild boy. I'm bet - ter than this,

G
F
I know my worth, I might be get - tin' what I de - serve.
Am
C
But I ain't stick - in' 'round for the re - run, what's done is done.
Am
C
And there goes the a - larm, ring - in' in my head like some - bo - dy
f
G
F
Am
C
said, 'Don't you trust him?' No. Text - in' from his ex, what did you ex -

G
F
-pect? Now you're ly - in' here know - in' where he goes. Now he got - ta
Am
C
G
F
get ya, Kar - ma's gon - na get ya, same way that they come, that's the way they go.
Am
C
To Coda
Now he got - ta get ya, re - wind - in' the pic - ture, there goes the a -
G
-larm and the si - ren's go, there goes the a -

Am
C
G
F
- larm.
mf
Am
C
G
F
1.
2.
There goes the a -
F
Am
Bang, bang, drums get high - er, man down, one fool, one li - ar.
mp

F
Em
Ring, ring, trust gone miss - in', house on fire,
house on fire.
F
Bang, bang, drums get high - er.
Am
Man down, one fool, one li - ar.
F
Ring, ring,
Em
trust gone miss - in', house on fire.
D.S. al Coda
And there goes the a -

Coda
G
F
-larm and the si - ren's go.
There goes the a -
Am
C
G
F
-larm, now he got - ta get ya. There goes the a - larm.
mf
Am
C
There goes the a - larm, now he got - ta get ya. There goes the a -
G
F
-larm,
there goes the a - larm.
p

Cold Water

Words & Music by Jamie Scott, Thomas Pentz, Benjamin Levin, Justin Bieber,
Ed Sheeran, Philip Meckseper, Henry Allen & Karen Orsted

C♯m
D
F♯m
A
Oh.
You should-n't be drown - ing on your own.
You should-n't be fight - ing on your own.
And if you feel you're sink-ing, I will jump right o - ver in - to
cold, cold wa - ter for you.
And al-though time may take us in - to
dif - fer-ent plac - es, I will still be pa-tient with you.
And I hope you

E5
N.C.
F♯m
A
C♯m
D
know, I won't let go.
I'll be your
life - line tonight.
I won't let
go.
I'll be your
1.
2.
life - line to - night.

F#m7
Aadd2
C#m7
Dsus2
Come on, come on, save me from my rock - ing boat. I just wan - na stay a -
-float. I'm all a - lone. And
I hope, I hope some-one's gon - na take me home, some-where I can rest my
soul. I need to know you won't let go.
N.C.
F#m
A

C♯m
D
F♯m
A
I'll be your life - line to - night.
You won't let go.
I'll be your
life - line to - night.
I won't let go.
I won't let go.
N.C.

Closer

Words & Music by Joseph King, Isaac Slade, Shaun Frank, Ashley Frangipane, Andrew Taggart & Frederic Kennett

Cadd9
D
Em7
D
D♭add9
E♭
Fm7
E♭
Hey, you tell your friends it was nice to meet them but I
Stay and play that Blink-one-eight-y-two song that we
hope I never see them again.
beat to death in Tucson, okay?
I know it breaks your heart, moved to the city in a broke-down car and
four years, no calls. Now you're looking pretty in a hotel bar and

Cadd9
D
Em7
D
D♭add9
E♭
Fm7
E♭
I, I can't stop. No,
I, I can't stop. So,
baby, pull me closer in the back seat of your Rover that I
know you can't afford. Bite that tattoo on your shoulder, pull the

Cadd9 D Em7 D
D♭add9 E♭ Fm7 E♭
sheets right off the cor - ner of that mat - tress that you stole from your
Cadd9 D Em7 D
D♭add9 E♭ To Coda Fm7 E♭
room - mate back in Boul - der, we ain't ev - er get - ting old - er.
Cadd9 D Em7 D Cadd9 D
D♭add9 E♭ Fm7 E♭ D♭add9 E♭
f
We ain't
Em7 D Cadd9 D Em7 D
Fm7 E♭ D♭add9 E♭ Fm7 E♭
ev - er get - ting old - er.

1.
2.
D.S. al Coda
Cadd9
D
Em7
D
Em7
D
D♭add9
E♭
Fm7
E♭
Fm7
E♭
We ain't ev - er get-ting old - er.
ev - er get-ting old - er. So,
Coda
Em7
D
Cadd9
D
Fm7
E♭
D♭add9
E♭
ev - er get - ting old - er, we ain't ev - er get - ting old - er, we ain't
1.
Em7
D
Cadd9
D
Em7
D
Fm7
E♭
D♭add9
E♭
Fm7
E♭
ev - er get-ting old - er, we ain't ev - er get-ting old - er, we ain't ev - er get-ting old - er, we ain't

2.
Em7 D Cadd9 D Em7 D
Fm7 E♭ D♭add9 E♭ Fm7 E♭
ev - er get - ting old - er.
f
Cadd9 D Em7 D Cadd9 D
D♭add9 E♭ Fm7 E♭ D♭add9 E♭
We ain't ev - er get - ting old - er.
Em7 D Cadd9 D Em7 D
Fm7 E♭ D♭add9 E♭ Fm7 E♭
We ain't ev - er get - ting old - er.
Cadd9 D Em7 D Cadd9 D Em7 D
D♭add9 E♭ Fm7 E♭ D♭add9 E♭ Fm7 E♭
p

Don't Wanna Know

Words & Music by Adam Levine, Benjamin Levin, Ammar Malik, Kurtis McKenzie, Jacob Hindlin, John Henry Ryan, Kendrick Lamar, Alexander Ben-Abdallah & Jonathan Mills

Em7
D/E
so, so, so, the way I used to love you. No, I don't wan-na know,
G/C
D
know, know, know who's tak-ing you home, home, home, home. I'm lov-ing you so,
Em7
D/E
so, so, so, the way I used to love you. Oh, I don't wan-na know.
G/C
D
Wast-ed, and the more I drink the more

Em7
D/E
I think a - bout you.
Oh, no, no, I can't
G/C
D
take it,
ba - by, ev - 'ry place I go
Em7
D/E
re - minds me of you.
Do you
G/C
D
Em7
think of me, of what we used to be?
Is it bet - ter now that I'm
mf

D/E
G/C
D
not a - round? My friends are act - in' strange, they don't bring up your name. Are you
Em7
D/E
hap - py now? Are you hap - py now? I don't wan - na know
G/C
D
know, know, know who's tak - ing you home, home, home, home. I'm lov - ing you so,
Em7
D/E
so, so, so, the way I used to love you. No, I don't wan - na know,

G/C
D
know, know, know who's tak - ing you home, home, home, home. I'm lov - ing you so,
Em7
D/E
To Coda
so, so, so, the way I used to love you. No, I don't wan - na know,
1.
and ev - 'ry time I go out, yeah, I hear it from this
Em7
D/E
one, I hear it from that one, that you got some - one new, yeah.

G/C
D
I see but don't_ be - lieve_ it,
e - ven in my_
Em7
D/E
_ head you're still in my_ bed, may - be I'm just_ a fool._ Do you
2.
G/C
D
_ Wast - ed,
and the more_ I drink_ the more_
mp
Em7
D/E
_ I think a - bout_ you.
Oh, no, no, I can't

G/C
D
take it.
Do you think that I should just
Em7
D.S. al Coda
go on with-out you?
No, I don't wan-na know
Coda
G/C
D
know, know, know who's tak-ing you home, home, home, home. I'm lov-ing you so,
Em7
D/E
so, so, so, the way I used to love you. No, I don't wan-na know,

G/C
D
know, know, know who's tak - ing you home, home, home, home. I'm lov - ing you so,
Em7
D/E
so, so, so, the way I used to love you. Oh, I don't wan - na know.
G/C
D
mp
Em7
D/E

I Believe In You

Words & Music by Alan Chang, Michael Bublé, Tom Jackson, Carl Wikstroem Ask, Magnus Nilsson, David Larson, Filip Bekic, Povel Olsson & Ryan Lerman

Bm7
Cm7
Em
Fm
when I'm with you,
oh,
Csus2
D♭sus2
G
A♭
D
E♭
you.
But I can see
how strong a
Em
Fm
Csus2
D♭sus2
man I'm gon - na have to be,
to do for
G
A♭
D
E♭
you what comes so na - tural - ly,
it's in the way you

Em
Fm
Csus2
D♭sus2
move.
Am
B♭m
D
E♭
G
A♭
G/B
A♭/C
And all I want is a chance to prove,
And all I want is to know you're near,
C
D♭
Am7
B♭m7
D
E♭
show all I can do.
you're all I need here.
G
A♭
C
D♭
I be-lieve in start-ing o-ver,
I can see that your heart is true,

G
A♭
D
E♭
I be - lieve in good things com - ing back to you.
Em
Fm
C
D♭
You're the light that lifts me high - er, so bright you guide me through.
1.
Em
C
Fm
D♭
G
A♭
I be - lieve in you.
And I don't mind
mp
D
E♭
Em
Fm
C
D♭
if you want to hold on - to me tight, you don't

G
A♭
D
E♭
have to sleep a - lone to - night
if you
Em
Fm
Csus2
D♭sus2
don't want to.
2.
Em
Fm
C
D♭
I be-lieve in you.
C
D♭
I know that there are times when you feel worth - less,
D
E♭
C
D♭
like all the love you get, you don't de-serve it.
Some-times I feel my

Cm
D♭m
faith is just a bur - den on you, you.
G
A♭
I be - lieve in start - ing o - ver,
C
D♭
I can see that your heart is true,
G
A♭
I be - lieve in love you give me
mp
D
E♭
rea - son to.
Em
Fm
You're the light that lifts me high - er,
C
D♭
so high up in the sky,

G
A♭
D
E♭
I, I think we're gon-na fly.
A
B♭
D
E♭
I be-lieve in start-ing o - ver, I can see that your heart is true,
f
A
B♭
E
F
I be-lieve in love you give me rea - son to.
F♯m
Gm
D
E♭
You're the light that lifts me high - er, so bright you guide me through,

F♯m
D
A
Gm
E♭
B♭
I be - lieve in you.
D
A
E
E♭
B♭
F
I be - lieve in you.
I be - lieve in you.
F♯m
D
F♯m
D
Gm
E♭
Gm
E♭
Whoa, you guide me through.
A
B♭
rit.
N.C.
I be - lieve in you.
p

Love On Me

Words & Music by Christian Lars Karlsson, Henrik Jonback, Richard Boardman, Sarah Blanchard, Linus Eklow, Jimmy Koitzsch, Anthony Maniscalco & Laura White

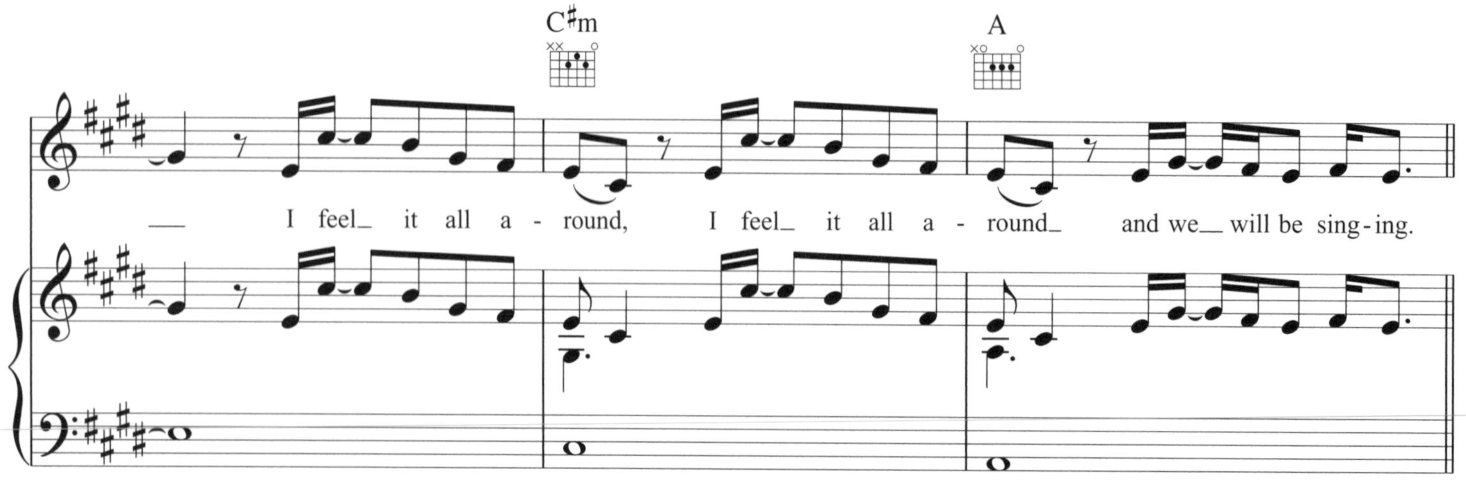

E
C♯m
A
And we will be sing-ing.
E
Ooh,
ooh,
C♯m
A
ooh
and we will be sing-ing.

E
Girl put your love on me 'cause I won't let you
C♯m
A
down, I won't let you down and we will be sing-ing.
E
Girl put your love on me, I feel it all a-
C♯m
A
-round, I feel it all a-round and we will be sing-ing.

E
C♯m
A
F♯m
(Sing - ing sing - ing sing - ing sing - ing sing - ing sing - ing sing - ing sing - ing
E
C♯m
A
F♯m
sing - ing sing - ing sing - ing sing - ing sing - ing.) And we___ will be sing - ing.
E
C♯m
A
F♯m
Ooh, ooh,
(Sing - ing sing - ing sing - ing sing - ing sing - ing sing - ing sing - ing sing - ing
E
C♯m
A
ooh and we___ will be sing - ing.
sing - ing sing - ing sing - ing sing - ing.)

E
C♯m
A
F♯m
Girl put your love on me 'cause I won't let you
E
C♯m
A
F♯m
down, I won't let you down and we will be sing-ing.
E
C♯m
A
F♯m
Girl put your love on me, I feel it all a-
B
F♯
A
F♯m
-round, I feel it all a-round and we will be sing-ing.

A
(Sing - ing sing - ing sing - ing sing - ing sing - ing.) And we will be sing - ing.
E
A
E
A
E
And we will be sing - ing.
A
B
F♯
A
To Coda
And we will be sing - ing.

E
C♯m
A
F♯m
(Sing - ing sing - ing sing - ing sing - ing.)
Girl put your love on me 'cause I won't let you
down, I won't let you down and we will be sing - ing.
Girl put your love on me, I feel it all a -

B
F♯
A
-round, I feel it all a - round and we will be sing - ing.
E
C♯m
A
F♯m
Girl put your love on me 'cause I won't let you
E
C♯m
A
F♯m
down, I won't let you down and we will be sing - ing.
E
C♯m
A
F♯m
Girl put your love on me, I feel it all a -

A/B
-round, I feel it all a - round and we will be sing - ing.
E
(Sing - ing sing - ing sing - ing sing - ing sing - ing sing - ing sing - ing sing - ing
sing - ing sing - ing sing - ing sing - ing sing - ing.) And we will be sing - ing.
Ooh,
ooh,

D.S. al Coda
ooh.
And we will be sing-ing.
Coda
E
A
E
Girl put your love on me 'cause I won't let you down, I won't let you
A
E
A
down and we will be sing-ing. Girl put your love on me, I feel it all a-
F♯m
A/B
-round, I feel it all a-round and we will be sing-ing.

The Mack

Words & Music by Mark Morrison, Willie Maxwell, Daniel Stephenson & Jonathan White

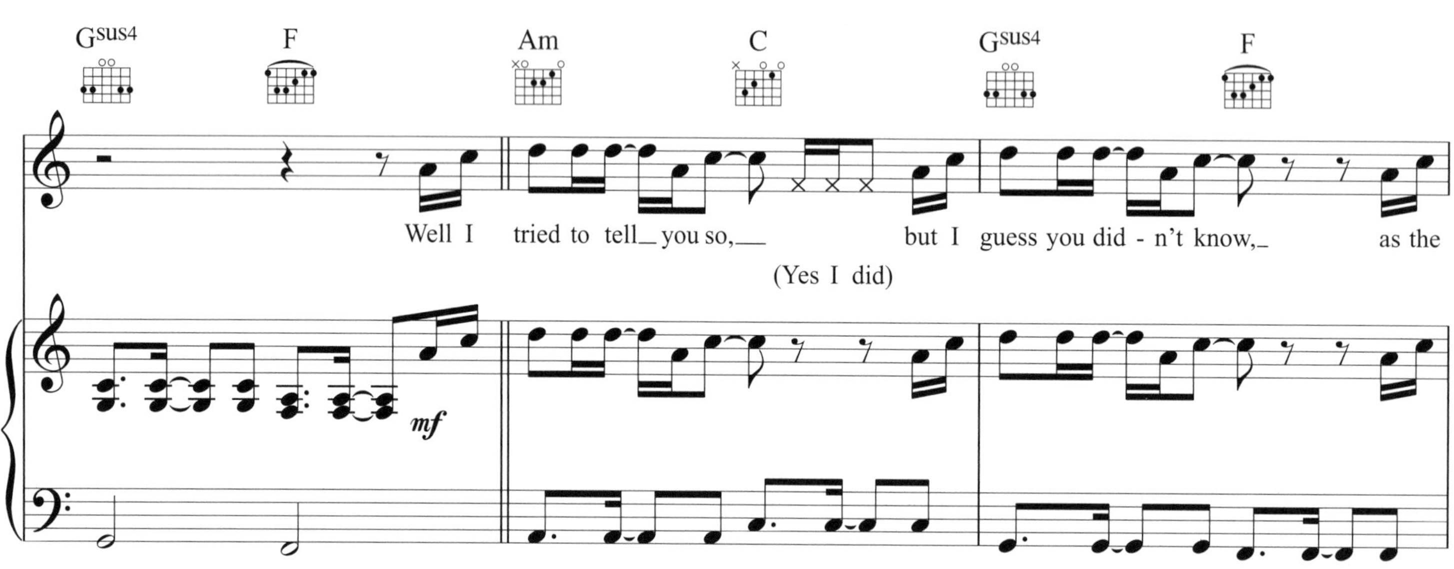

Am
C
Gsus4
F
know it from the start, ba - by, when you broke my heart, that I
had to come a - gain and show you that I'm with. You
lied to me, all those times I said that I loved you, you
lied to me.
Oh my God, ba - by, here I am. Re -

Am
C
Gsus4
F
-turn of The Mack, once a-gain, re - turn of The Mack, re -
Top of the world,
Am
C
Gsus4
F
-turn of The Mack, you know that I'll be back.
Watch my flow
Am
C
G
F
f
Am
C
Gsus4
F
Re - turn of The Mack. So I'm
mf

Am
C
Gsus4
F
back up in the game, run-ning things to keep my swing, let-ting
Hust - ling slow, whole night long,
all the peo - ple know that I'm back to run the show. 'Cause what you
did, you know, was wrong and all the nas - ty things you've done, so, ba - by,
(Oh, oh, oh, oh.)
lis - ten care - ful - ly while I sing my come - back song. You
(Squah!)

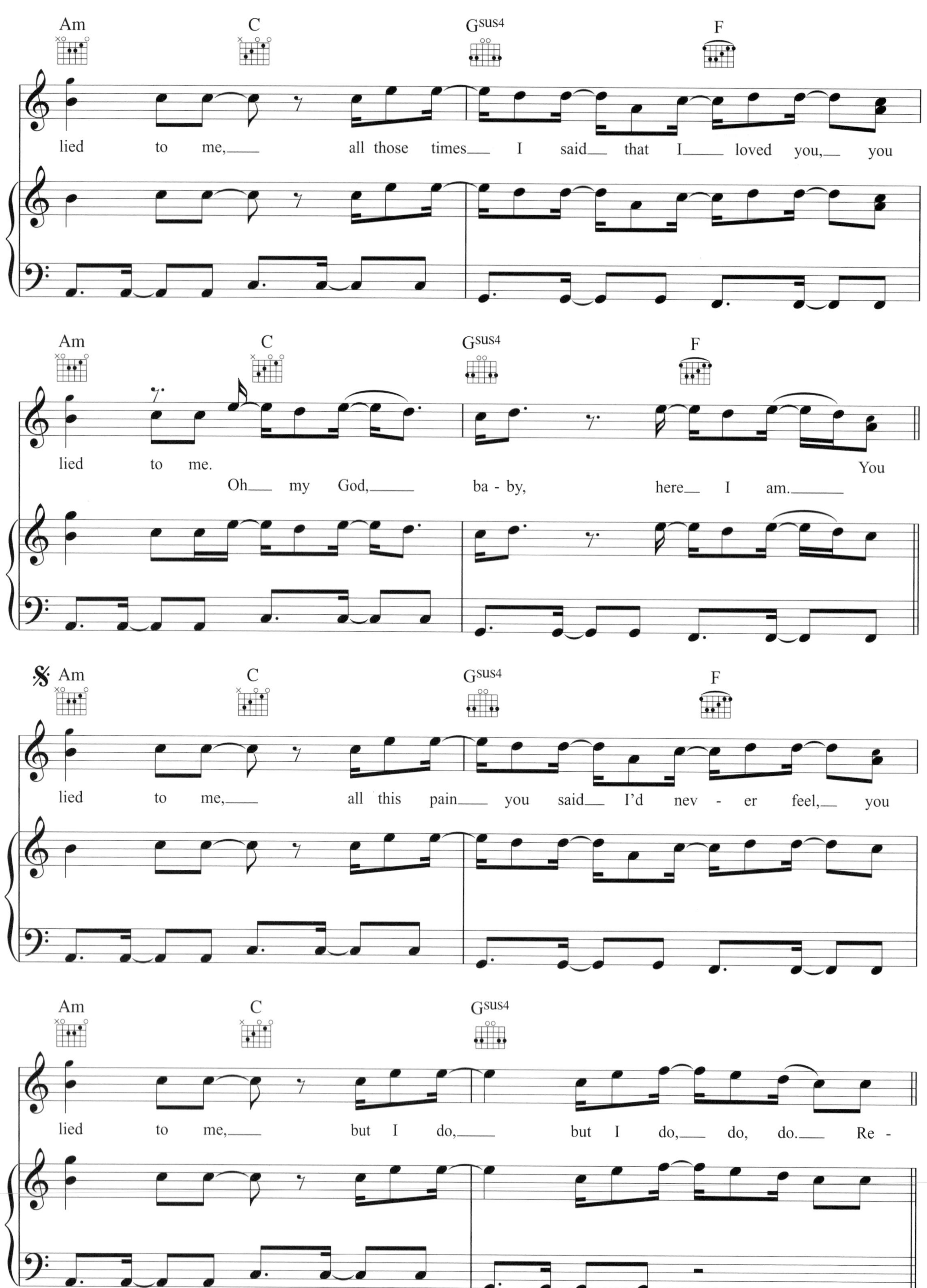
Am
C
Gsus4
F
lied to me, all those times I said that I loved you, you
Am
C
Gsus4
F
lied to me.
Oh my God, baby, here I am.
You
Am
C
Gsus4
F
lied to me, all this pain you said I'd nev - er feel, you
Am
C
Gsus4
lied to me, but I do, but I do, do, do. Re -

Am C Gsus4 F
-turn of The Mack, re - turn of The Mack, re -
There it is Come on
Am C Gsus4 F
-turn of The Mack, you know that I'll be back. Re -
Oh my God Here I am
Am C Gsus4 F
-turn of The Mack, re - turn of The Mack, re -
Once a - gain Top of the world
Am C Gsus4 F
To Coda
-turn of The Mack, you know that I'll be back. 'Cause the
Watch my flow.

Am
C
Gsus4
F
mo - ney ain't e - nough, I re - mem - ber when it was. I had
dreams of giv - ing up, I ain't nev - er leave you stuck. And
you say you will ne - ver turn on me, ba - by, aye, you played me like a tour - na - ment, ba - by,
aye, you know I gave you the best of me ba - by. Oh, man, I thought that you were next to me, ba - by. I

Am
C
guess I got - ta show you I'm the one that you were with, that got you
Gsus4
F
swer - ving in the whip and put - ting com - mas on your wrists,
Am
C
Gsus4
F
D.S. al Coda
babe, still mak-ing hit af - ter hit, babe, I bet you let me hit af - ter this. You
Coda
G
F
know that I'll be back, here I go.

Rockabye

Words & Music by Steve McCutcheon, Sean Henriques, Ina Wroldsen, Ammar Malik & Jack Patterson

Am
F
E
ANNE-MARIE:
Ban - dit, Sean - da - Paul, Anne - Ma - rie sing, make them hear. She works the nights,
Am
F
G
Em
by the wa - ter. She's gon - na stress,
Am
F
G
Em
so far a - way from her fa - ther's daugh - ter, she just wants a life
Am
F
G
Em
for her ba - by. All on her own,

Am F G Em
SEAN PAUL:
ANNE-MARIE:
no one will come, she's got to save him. (Dai - ly strug - gle.) She tells him;
Am F G Em
'Oh, love, no - one's ev - er gon - na hurt you, love, I'm gon - na give you all of
Am F G Em
my love, no - bo - dy mat - ters like you.' She tells him;
(Stay out there, stay out there.)
Am F G Em
1. 3. 'your life ain't gon' be noth - ing like my life, you're going to grow and have a
2. 'Oh, love, no - one's ev - er gon - na hurt you, love, I'm gon - na give you all of

Am
F
G
Em
To Coda
good life, I'm gon - na do what I got to do.' So,
my love, no - bo - dy mat-ters like you.' (Stay out there, stay out there.)
Am
F
G
Em
rock - a - bye ba - by, rock - a - bye, I'm gon - na rock you.
Am
F
G
Em
Rock - a - bye ba - by, don't you cry, some - bo - dy's got you.
Am
F
G
Em
Rock - a - bye ba - by, rock - a - bye, I'm gon - na rock you.

Am
F
Rock - a - bye ba - by, don't you cry, rock - a - bye,
Am
F
G
Em
no.
Rock - a - bye
(Rock - a - bye, rock - a, rock - a, rock - a - bye.)
f
Am
F
G
yeah. (Rock - a - bye, rock - a, rock - a, rock - a - bye.)
1.
Am
F
G
Em
SEAN PAUL:
Sin - gle ma - ma you do - ing out there,
fac - ing the hard life with-out no fear.
ANNE-MARIE: (Yeah.)
mp

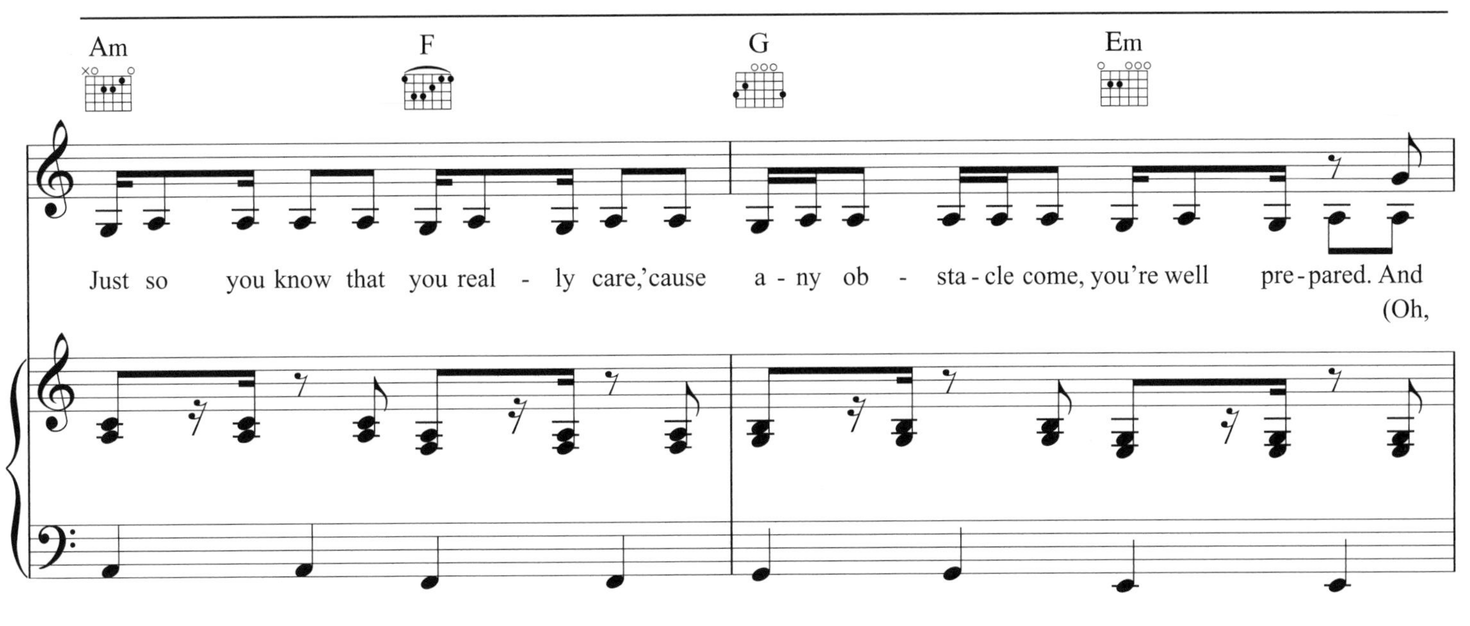
Am
F
G
Em
Just so you know that you real - ly care,'cause a - ny ob - sta - cle come, you're well pre - pared. And
(Oh,

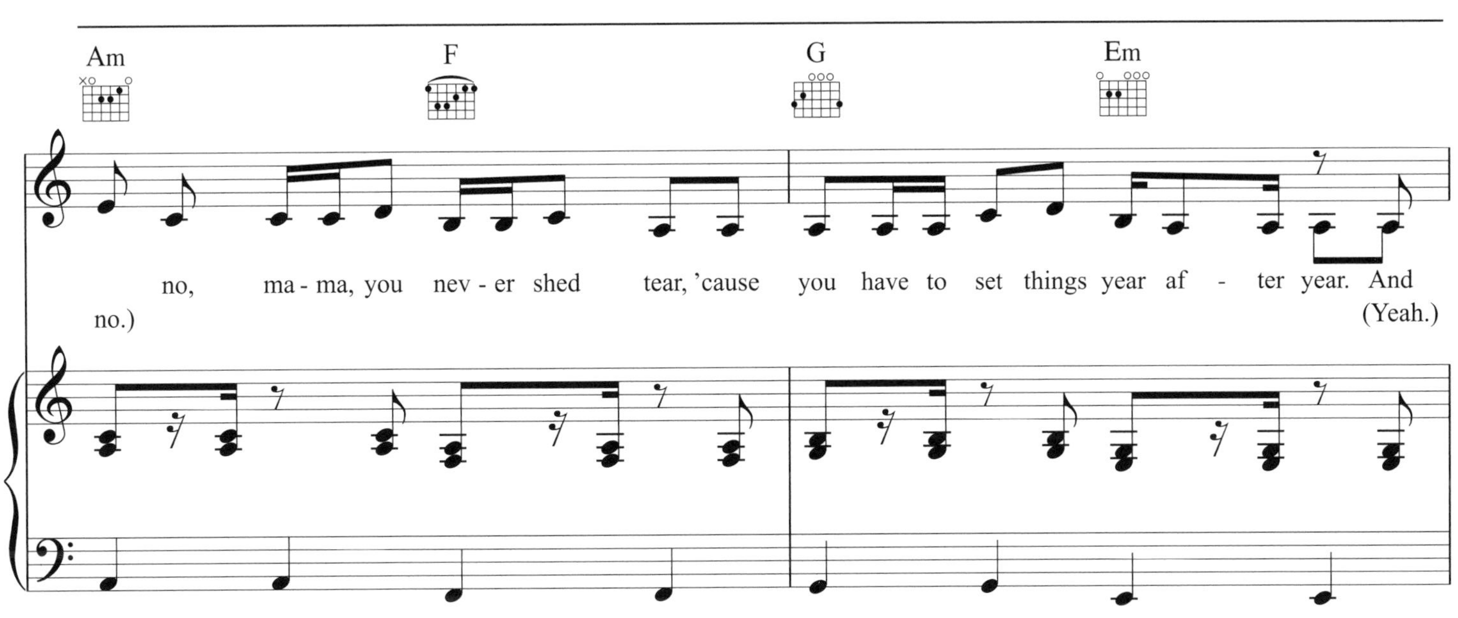
Am
F
G
Em
no, ma - ma, you nev - er shed tear, 'cause you have to set things year af - ter year. And
no.)
(Yeah.)

Am
F
G
you give the youth love be - yond com - pare,_ you find his school fee and the bus fare._
(Yeah.)

Am
F
G
Em
Mmm, Ma - rie, the paps dis - ap - pear in the round back can't find him no - where.
Am
F
G
Stead - i - ly you work flow ev - 'ry - thing you know, so you nuh stop, no time, no time fi a jear.
Am
F
G
Em
ANNE-MARIE:
Now she got a six - year - old, try'n' to keep him warm, try'n' to keep out the
Am
F
G
Em
cold. When he looks in her eyes, he don't know he is safe, when she says;

2.
Am
F
G
Em
SEAN PAUL:
Rock - a - bye, don't bo - ther cry. Lift up your head, lift it up to the sky, yo.
Am
F
G
Rock - a - bye, don't bo - ther cry. An - gels sur - round you, just dry your eye.
Am
F
G
Em
ANNE-MARIE:
Now she got a six - year - old, try'n' to keep him warm, try'n' to keep out the
p
F
E
D.S. al Coda
cold. When he looks in her eyes, he don't know he is safe. When she says… She tells him;

Coda
Am
F
G
ANNE-MARIE:
Rock - a - bye ba - by, rock - a - bye, I'm gon - na rock you.
SEAN PAUL: (Rock - a - bye, rock - a - rock - a - rock - a - bye.)
1.
Am
F
G
Rock - a - bye ba - by, don't you cry, some - bo - dy's got you.
(Rock - a - bye, rock - a - rock - a - rock - a - bye.)
2.
G
Em
Rock - a - bye,
(Bad - da bang, bang, bang, al - right then.)

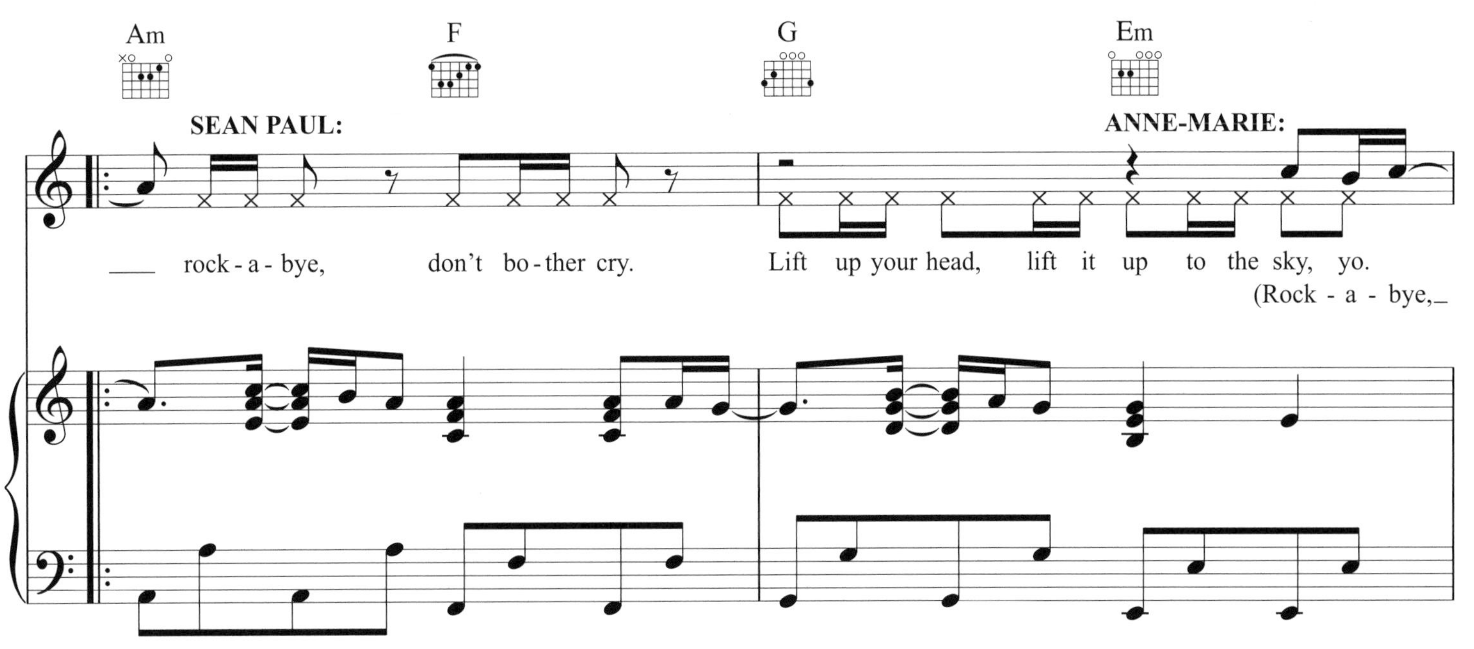
Am
F
G
Em
SEAN PAUL:
ANNE-MARIE:
rock - a - bye, don't bo - ther cry. Lift up your head, lift it up to the sky, yo.
(Rock - a - bye,

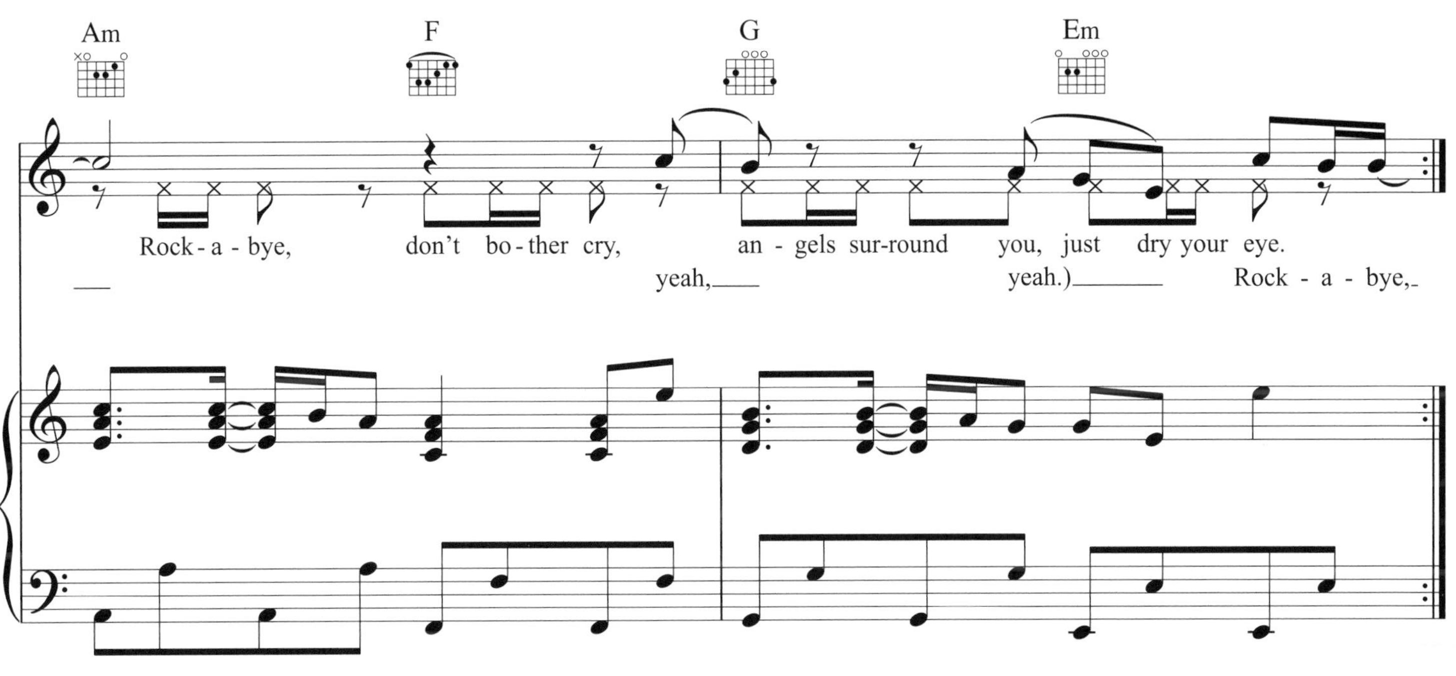
Am
F
G
Em
Rock - a - bye, don't bo - ther cry, an - gels sur-round you, just dry your eye.
yeah, yeah.) Rock - a - bye,

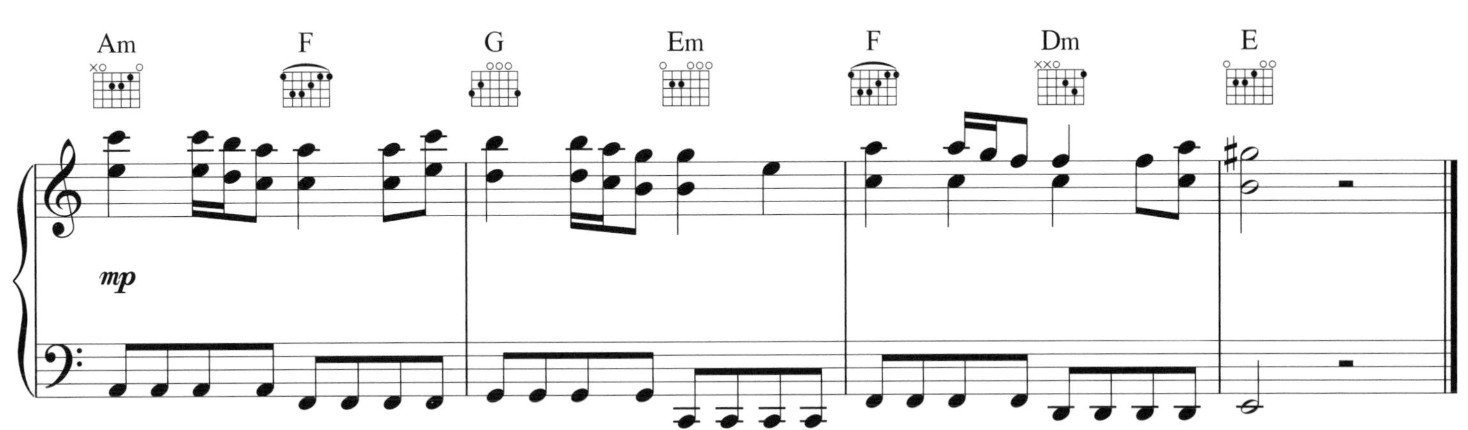
Am
F
G
Em
F
Dm
E
mp

Let Me Love You

Words & Music by Justin Bieber, William Grigahcine, Brian Lee, Steven Marsden,
Andrew Wotman, Carl Rosen, Teddy Mendez & Edwin Perez

Am7
C
F
Cm7
E♭
A♭
smoke and mir - rors keep us wait - ing on a mi - ra - cle, on a
is a rude a - wak - en - ing to know we're good e - nough, know we're
Am
Cm
mi - ra - cle.
good e - nough.
Say, go through the dark - est of days, hea - ven's a heart - break a - way.
G
Dm7
F
B♭
Fm7
A♭
Nev - er let you go, nev - er let me down.
Oh, it's been a hell of a ride,
Am
G
Dm7
Cm
B♭
Fm7
driv - ing the edge of a knife. Nev - er let you go, nev - er let me down.
Don't you give up,

Am7
Cm7
Cmaj7
E♭maj7
— nah, — nah, nah. I won't give up, — nah, — nah, nah. Let — me
C/E
F
E♭/G
A♭
love you, — let — me love you. — Don't you give up, — nah, — nah, nah. I won't give up, —
— nah, — nah, nah. Let — me love you, — let — me love you. —
C
E♭
f

C/E
F
E♭/G
A♭
Am7
Cm7
C
E♭
1.
2.
2. Don't fall a - sleep
C5
E♭5
(Nev - er let you go, nev - er let me down. Nev - er let you go, nev - er let me down.
Nev - er let you go, I'll nev - er let you go.)

2.
C/E
F
E♭/G
A♭
Am7
Cm7
Cmaj7
E♭maj7
Don't you give up, nah, nah, nah, I won't give up, nah, nah, nah. Let me
love you, let me love you. Don't you give up, nah, nah, nah. I won't give up,
nah, nah, nah. Let me love you, let me love you.

Say You Won't Let Go

Words & Music by James Arthur, Neil Ormandy & Steven Solomon

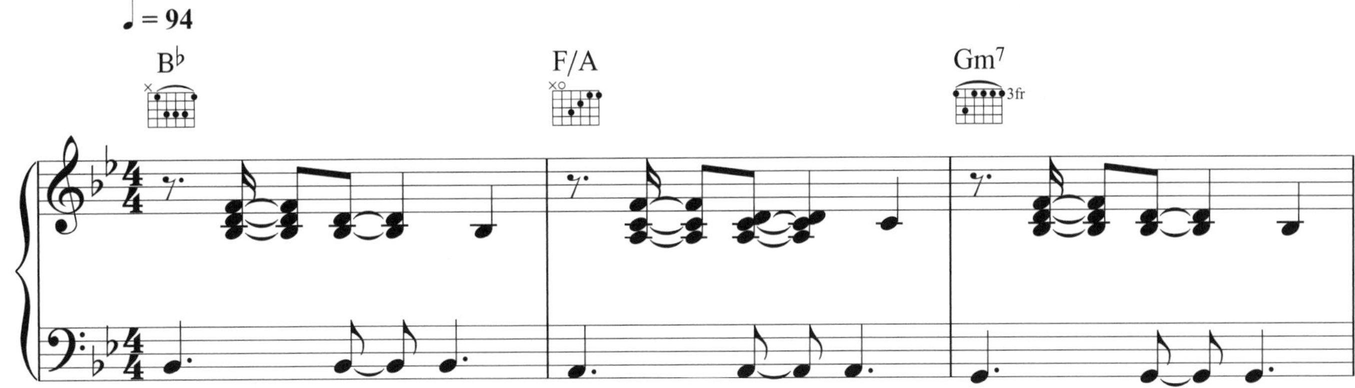

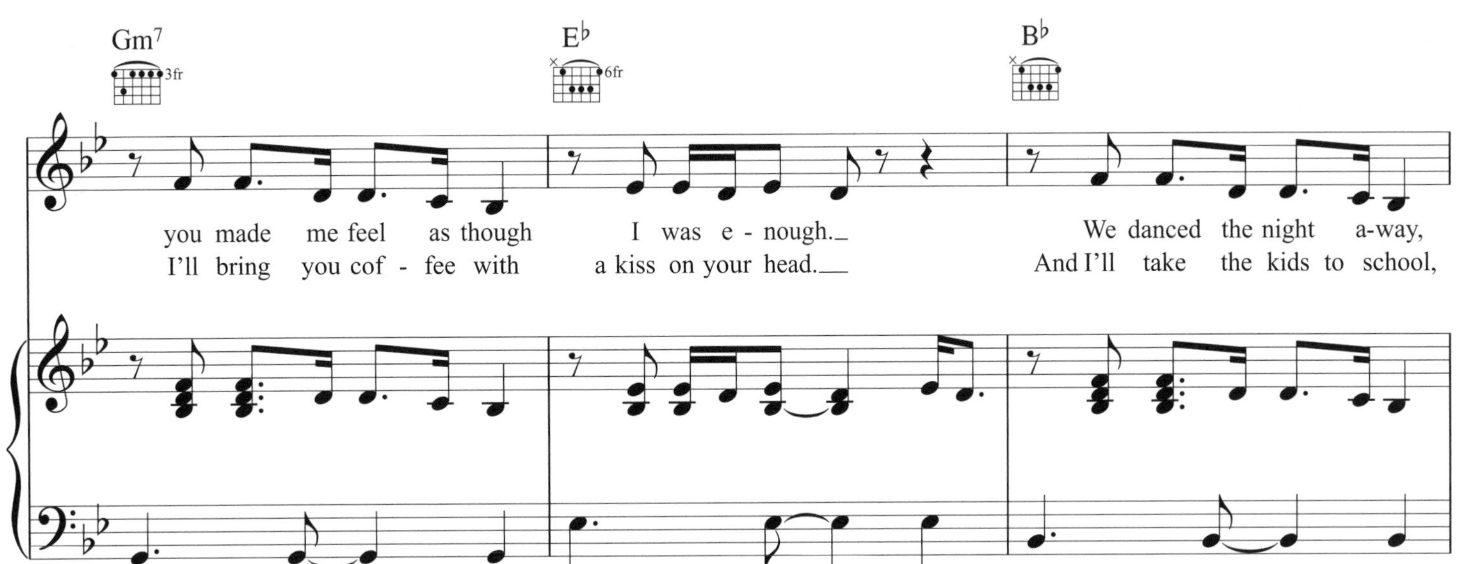

F/A
Gm7
3fr
E♭
6fr
we drank too much, I held your hair back when you were throw-ing up.
wave them good-bye and I'll thank my luck-y stars for that night.
B♭
F/A
Then you smiled o-ver your shoul-der for a min-ute, I was stone cold so-ber
When you looked o-ver your shoul-der for a min-ute, I for-get that I'm old-er
Gm7
3fr
E♭
6fr
B♭
I pulled you clos-er to my chest. And you asked me to stay o-ver,
I wan-na dance with you right now. Oh and you look as beau-ti-ful as ev-er
F/A
Gm7
3fr
E♭
6fr
I said, I al-rea-dy told ya I think that you should get some rest.
and I swear that ev-'ry day you'll get bet-ter, you make me feel this way some-how.

B♭
F/A
Gm7
3fr
I knew I loved you then but you'd nev - er know 'cause I played it cool when I was
I'm so in love with you and I hope you know, dar-ling your love is more than
I'm gon - na love you till my lungs give out, I pro-mise till death we part
E♭
6fr
B♭
F/A
scared of let - ting go. I know I need-ed you but I nev - er showed,
worth its weight in gold. We've come so far my dear, look how we've grown
like in our vows. So I wrote this song for you, now ev-'ry-bo - dy knows
Gm7
3fr
E♭
6fr
B♭
but I wan - na stay with you un - til we're grey and old.
and I wan - na stay with you un - til we're grey and old.
that it's just you and me un - til we're grey and old.
Just say you won't let go.

F/A
Gm7
3fr
To Coda
E♭
6fr
Just say you won't let go.
B♭
F
I wan - na live with you e - ven when we're ghosts
Gm7
3fr
E♭
6fr
D.S. al Coda
'cause you were al - ways there for me when I need - ed you most.

⊕ *Coda*

Gm7
3fr
E♭
6fr
say you won't let go.
Just

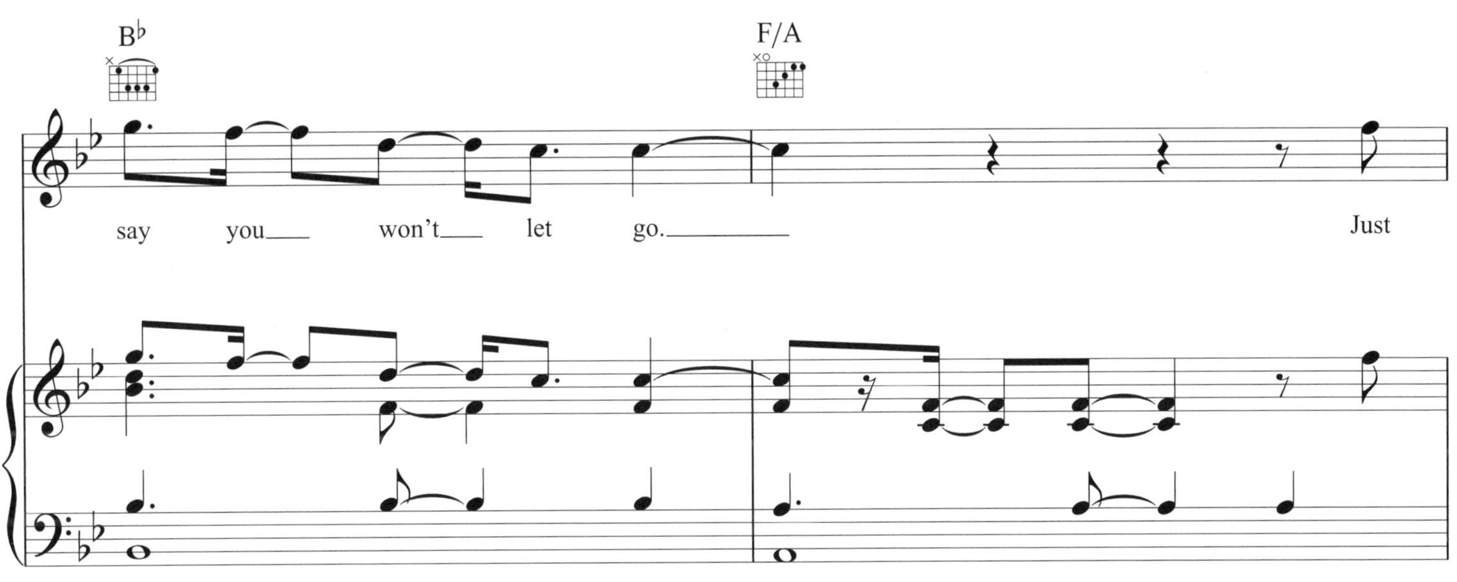

B♭
F/A
say you won't let go.
Just

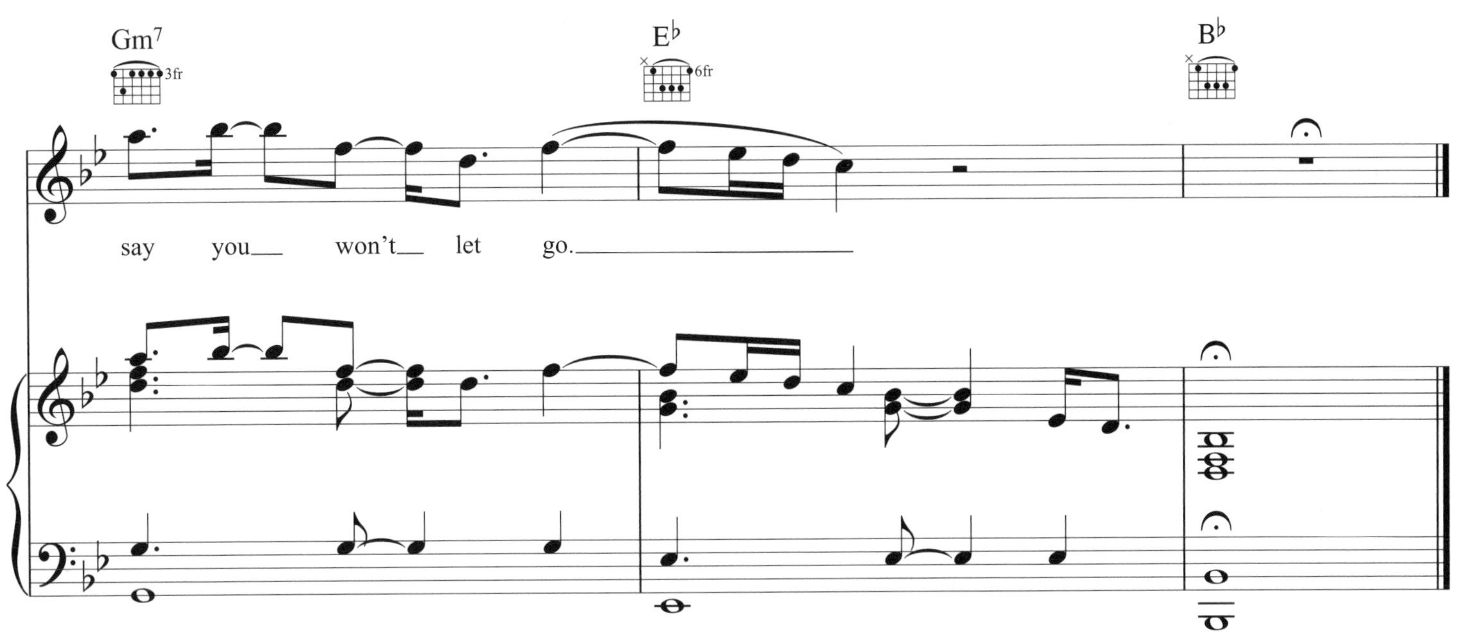

Gm7
3fr
E♭
6fr
B♭
say you won't let go.

Sexual

Words & Music by Victor Raadstroem, Elina Stridh & Oladayo Olatunji

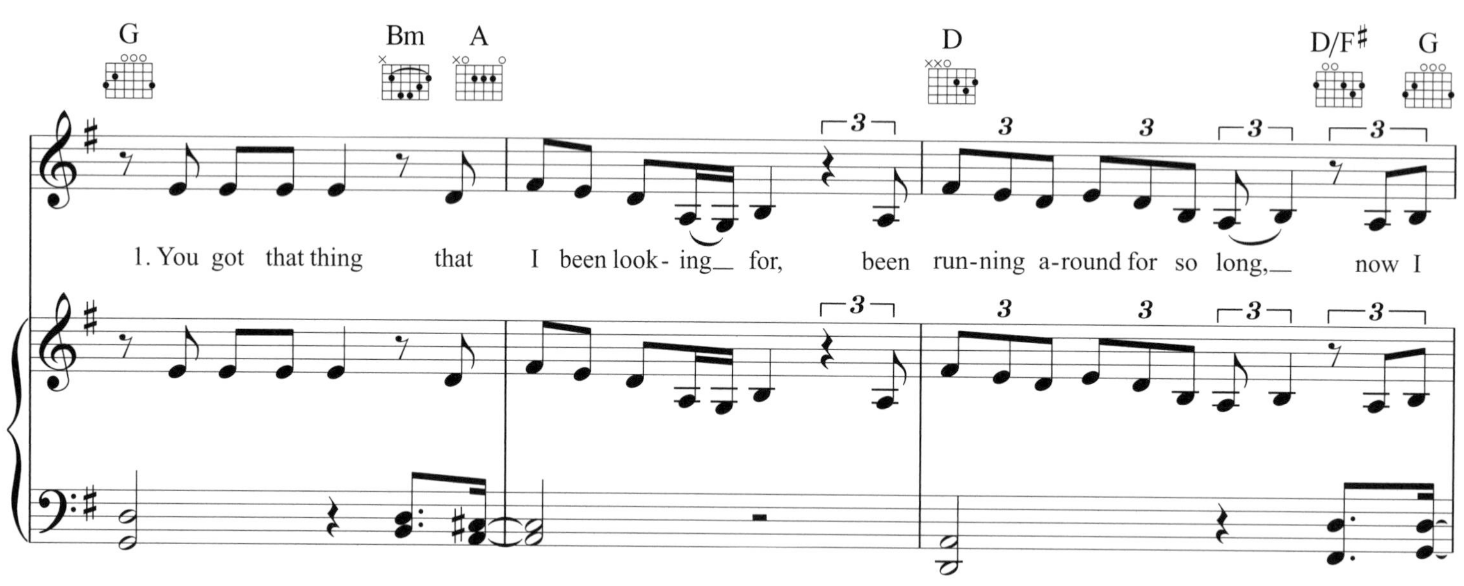

D
D/F♯
G
you got a heart full of gold and that's real - ly turn - ing me on.
G
Bm
A
You are, you are, you are, you are, you are
D
D/F♯
G
ev - 'ry - thing that I dreamed of, now we can paint a pic - ture.
Bm
A
You are, you are, you are, you are, you are

D
D/F♯
G
mak - ing my life much green - er,
yeah, yeah.
G
Bm
A
Just say you feel the way that I feel,
mf
D
D/F♯
G
To Coda ⊕
I'm feel - ing sex - u - al, so we should be sex - u - al.
G
Bm
A
3
2. You got some - thing that I ain't seen be - fore, you've

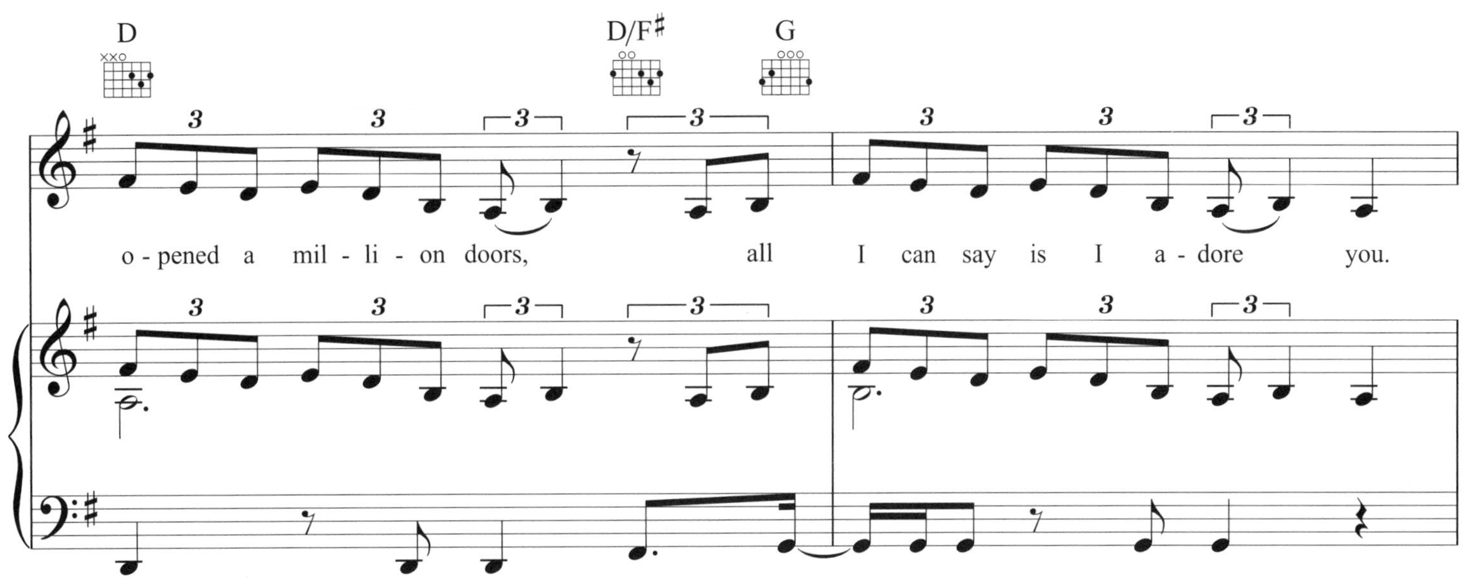
D
D/F♯
G
o - pened a mil - li - on doors, all I can say is I a - dore you.

Bm
A
D
D/F♯
G
You got some-thing that I ain't seen be - fore, hold me 'cause ba - by, I'm yours, oh, I

D.S. al Coda
with repeats
Coda
G
Bm
A
can't wait un-til we get home.
f

D
D/F#
G
1.
2.
I don't
G
Bm
A
know what you done but I can't get e - nough.
D
D/F#
G
mp
Bm
A
'Cause you give me that rush, I don't want it to stop.
D
D/F#
G

G
Bm
A
Just say you feel the way that I feel,
mf
D
D/F♯
G
I'm feel-ing sex - u - al, so we should be sex - u - al.
G
Bm
A
f
D
D/F♯
G
3
3
3
3
3
3

Side To Side

Words & Music by Savan Kotecha, Max Martin, Alexander Kronlund, Onika Maraj, Ilya & Ariana Grande

D E F#m C#m E
bo - dy and we don't got - ta think_ 'bout noth - in'. ('Bout noth - in'.) I'm com - in' at ya
so - lo, just as long as you know_ you got___ me. (You got__ me.) And boy I got ya
F#m C#m E F#m C#m E
'cause I know you got a bad re - pu - ta - tion, does - n't mat - ter, 'cause you give me temp -
'cause to - night I'm mak - ing deals with the dev - il and I know it's gon - na get me in
D E F#m
- ta - tion and we don't got - ta think_ 'bout noth - in'. ('Bout noth - in'.) These
trou - ble just as long as you know_ you got___ me.
N.C.
friends keep talk - in' way too much, say I should give you up, can't hear them, no, 'cause

F♯m
C♯m
4fr
E
I…
I've been here all
night,
I've been here all
F♯m
C♯m
E
D
E
day
and
boy,
got me walk-in' side
to
F♯m
C♯m
E
F♯m
C♯m
E
side.
I've been here all
night,
I've been here all
day
and
1.
D
E
F♯m
boy,
got me walk-in' side
to
side.
(Side
to
side.)
Been try-na hide it

2.
F#m
C#m
4fr
E
side. (Side to side.) This the new style with the fresh type of flow,
D
wrist i - ci - cle, ride dick bi - cy - cle, come true yo, get you this type of blow, if
you wan-na Min-aj I got a tri - cy - cle. All these bitch-es, flows is my mi - ni - me, bo - dy smok-ing
so they call me young Nick - i chi - mi - ney. Rap-pers in they feel-ings 'cause they feel - in' me, uh, I - I

F♯m
C♯m
4fr
give ze - ro fucks and I got ze - ro chill in me. Kiss-ing me, copped the blue box__ that say Tif - fa - ny,
F♯m
C♯m
D
E
cur - ry with the shot, just tell'em to call me Ste-pha-nie, gun pop and I make my gum pop, I'm the queen of
F♯m
N.C.
rap, young A - ri - a - na run pop. These friends keep talk - in' way too much, say I should give him
up, can't hear them, no, 'cause I... I've been there all

F♯m
C♯m
E
4fr
night,
I've been here all
day
and
(Been here all night ba - by.)
(Been here all day ba - by.)
D
1.
boy,
got me walk-in' side to side.
(Side to side.)
I've been here all
2.
side.
(Side to side.)
This the new style with the fresh type of flow,
wrist i - ci-cle, ride dick bi - cy - cle, come
true yo,
get you this type of blow,
if you wan-na Min - aj I got a tri - cy - cle.

So Good

Words & Music by Steve Mac, Edward Drewett & Chelcee Grimes

Fm
Cm/E♭
I told my-self I'll be back by ten,
try - na save my-self for the week - end,
B♭7/D
B♭m
Cm
3fr
but I know me, I hate to miss a par - ty.
(Yeah, yeah, yeah.)
Fm
Cm/E♭
Don't say, don't say I did - n't warn you,
don't say I did - n't warn you.
B♭7/D
B♭m7
N.C.
3
Uh - huh. I live for the mo - ment. I was - n't sup-posed to go
f

Fm
Fm/E♭
out to-night.
I should be at home, I got
work at nine.
Should-n't be out here do-ing
B♭9/D
B♭m7
E♭
what I like,
but it feels so
good,
so
good.
Fm
Fm/E♭
I was on-ly gon-na be an
hour or two.
I guess that now I'm here I'm go-ing
B♭9/D
B♭m7
Cm7
3fr
down with you,
but it feels so
good,
so
good.

Fm
Cm/E♭
2. An-gel on my shoul-der's giv-ing up on me,
no list-en-ing to him and I can hard-ly speak.
mf
3
B♭/D
B♭m
E♭
The mu - sic they play,
makes me this way.
Oh,
yeah.
It was on-ly ten, how did it get to three?
It's like I'm in my own time ma-chine,
but you know me,
I nev - er leave.

Fm
Cm/E♭
Don't say, don't say I did-n't warn you,
don't say I did-n't warn you.
B♭/D
B♭m
N.C.
Just live for the mo - ment. I was-n't sup-posed to go
Fm
Fm/E♭
out to-night. I should be at home, I got work at nine. Should-n't be out here do-ing
B♭9/D
B♭m7
E♭
what I like, but it feels so good, so good.

Fm
Fm/E♭
I was on-ly gon-na be an hour or two.
I guess that now I'm here I'm go-ing

B♭9/D
B♭m7
Cm7
3fr
down with you,
but it feels so good,
so good.
'Cause

B♭m7
ev - 'ry - one I know is here,
drink - ing sours,
cry - ing tears,
mf

Fm
Fm7/E♭
liv-ing out the best years.
(Woah)
So keep on toast-ing shots. 'Cheers.' Peo-ple know it feels
(sopra)
B♭/D
N.C.
so good.
I was-n't sup-posed to go
Fm
Fm/E♭
(lead vocal ad lib.)
out to-night,
I should be at home, I got
work at nine.
Should-n't be out here do-ing

B♭9/D
B♭m7
E♭
what I like, but it feels so good, so good.

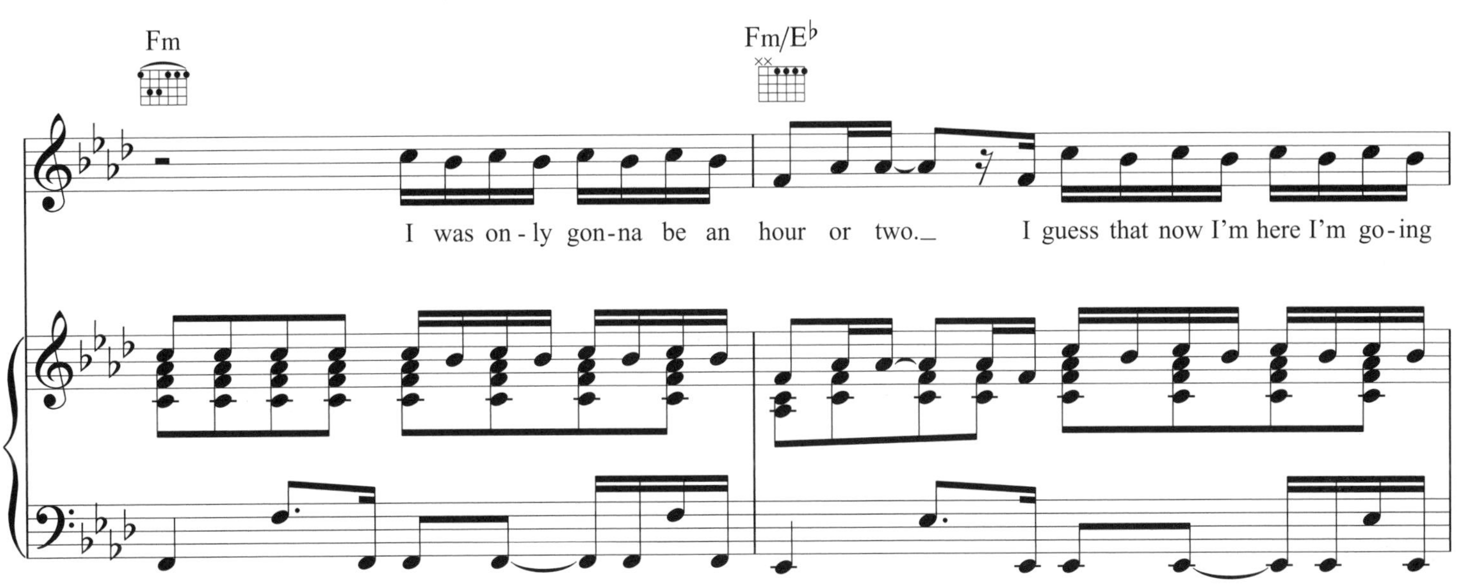
Fm
Fm/E♭
I was on-ly gon-na be an hour or two. I guess that now I'm here I'm go-ing

B♭9/D
B♭m7
Cm7
3fr
N.C.
down with you, but it feels so good, so good, so good.

Shout Out To My Ex

Words & Music by Iain James, Jessica Nelson, Jade Thirlwall, Perrie Edwards, Leigh-Anne Pinnock, Edvard Erfjord, Henrik Michelsen & Camille Purcell

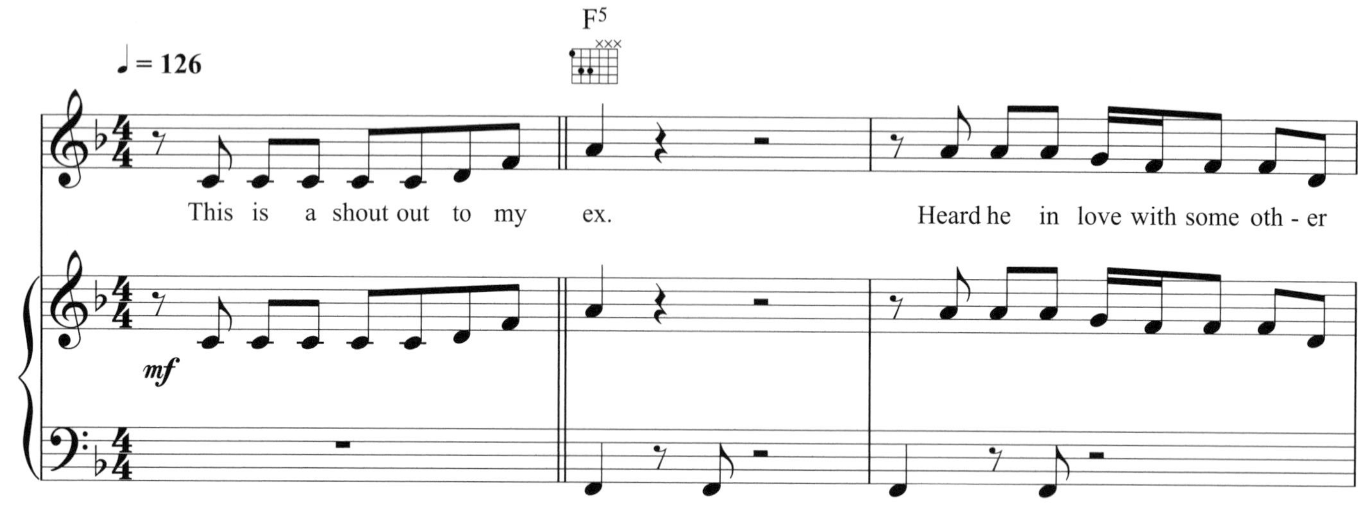

G5
3fr
B♭5
6fr
did, babe._ Took four long years to call it quits, for-get that boy I'm o - ver
F5
F5
it. Guess I should say thank_ you_ for the hate_ you's_ and the
G5
3fr
3
tat - toos,_ oh ba - by. I'm cool by the way, ain't sure I loved
B♭5
6fr
Dm
C
you an - y - way. Go 'head babe I'm - a live my life, my life,____ yeah._

F
Csus4
B♭
Shout out to my ex, you're real - ly quite the man, you made my heart break and that
made me who I am.
Here's to my ex, hey, look at me now. Well I,
I'm all the way up, I swear you'll nev-er bring me down.
Shout out to my ex, you're
real - ly quite the man, you made my heart break and that made me who I am.

Dm7
Csus4
B♭
Here's to my ex, hey, look at me now. Well I, I'm all the way up, I swear you'll
Csus4
To Coda N.C.
nev - er, you'll nev - er bring me down. Oh, I de - le - ted all your
mf
F
Gm
3fr
pics, then blocked your num-ber from my phone. Yeah, yeah, you took all you could
B♭
F
get, but you ain't get-ting this love no more.

N.C.
F
'Cause now I'm liv - ing so le - git,
e - ven though you broke my heart in
Gm
two, ba - by,
but I snapped right back I'm so brand
B♭
new, ba - by.
Boy, read my lips I'm o - ver
F
you. (O - ver you.)
Guess I should say
F
thank you for the hate you's and the tat - toos, oh ba - by. I'm

Gm
3fr
B♭
3
cool, by the way, ain't sure I loved you a-ny-way.
3
Dm
C
D.S. al Coda
Go 'head babe I'm-a live my life, my life, yeah.
Coda
F
Csus4
B♭
Ooh, ooh, you'll nev-er bring me
(down.)
Dm7
Csus4
B♭
Csus4
ooh, ooh, yeah.
(down.)

F
Csus4
B♭
Shout out to my ex, you're real - ly quite the man, you made my heart break and that
mp
Dm7
Csus4
made me who I am. Here's to my ex, hey, look at me now. Well I'm
B♭
Csus4
F
all the way up, I swear you'll nev - er, you'll nev - er bring me down.
F
Csus4
B♭
Shout out to my ex, you're real - ly quite the man, you made my heart break and that
f

F
Csus4
made me who I am. Here's to my ex, hey, look at me now. Well I,
B♭
F
I'm all the way up, I swear you'll nev-er bring me down. Shout out to my ex, you're
Csus4
B♭
real - ly quite the man, you made my heart break and that
Dm7
Csus4
made me who I am. Here's to my ex, hey, look at me now. Well I,

B♭
Csus4
I'm all the way up, I swear you'll nev - er, you'll nev - er bring me…
F
Csus4
B♭
Woah oh, oh woah, woah oh, oh woah. Woah oh, oh woah,
Dm7
Csus4
woah oh, oh woah. Woah oh, oh woah, woah oh, oh woah.
B♭
Csus4
F
Oh, oh, you'll nev - er bring me down.

Still Falling For You

Words & Music by Johan Schuster, Elena Goulding, Rickard Goransson, Ilya & Tove Lo

G♭
A♭
4fr
roll - ing the dice,
don't let me lose.
Still fall - ing for you.
D♭
4fr
Still fall - ing for you.
D♭
4fr
Beau - ti - ful mind, your heart got a sto - ry with mine, your heart got me
Bright - er than gold, this love shin - ing bright - er than gold, this love is like
B♭m
hurt - ing at times, your heart gave me new kind of highs, your heart got me
let - ters in bold, this love is like out of con - trol, this love's nev - er

G♭
A♭
4fr
feel - ing so fine, so what to do. Still fall - ing for you.
grow - ing old, you make it new. Still fall - ing for you.
D♭
4fr
Still fall - ing for you. It took us a while
Still fall - ing for you. It took us a while
with ev - 'ry breath a new day with love on the line.
'cause we were young and un - sure with love on the line.
B♭m
We've had our share of mis - takes but
What if we both would need more? but

D♭/G♭
A♭sus4
A♭
all your flaws and scars are mine. Still fall-ing for you.
all your flaws and scars are mine. Still fall-ing for you.
D♭
Still fall-ing for you.
Still fall-ing for you.
And just like
B♭m
G♭
that, all I breathe, all I feel
D♭
A♭
you are all for me. I'm in and just like

B♭m
G♭
that, all I breathe, all I feel
D♭
To Coda
A♭
G♭
you are all for me. No one can lift me, catch me the way that you do,
1.
A♭
D♭
I'm still fall-ing for you.
2.
A♭
D♭/G♭
D♭/E♭
B♭m
A♭
I'm still fall-ing for you. (Ooh) Fall-ing, crash in - to my arms.

D♭/G♭
D♭/E♭
D♭
A♭/C
D♭/G♭
D♭/E♭
4fr
3fr
(Ooh)
Love you like this, like a first kiss, nev-er let go.
(Ooh)
B♭m
A♭
G♭
A♭
Fall-ing, crash in - to my arms, nev-er break-ing what we got.
Still fall-ing for
D♭
D.S. al Coda
you,
still fall-ing for…
And just like
Coda
A♭
B♭m
(All for me.)
And just like that all I feel is you,

G♭
D♭
4fr
all I feel is you.
You are all for me,
1.
2.
A♭
4fr
I'm still fall - ing... And just like
no one can lift me, catch me the
G♭
A♭
4fr
way that you do.
I'm still fall - ing for you.
D♭
4fr

Sunshine

Words & Music by Mark Tieku & Daniel Ankrah

Am7
Em
Am7
Em
me. You're so ev - er so high, you fill my heart with a
Am7
Em
D
Em7
D/F♯
G
joy, you are ev - 'ry - thing now that I've found
Am7
Em
Am7
Em
you. I just want you to know, there's noth - ing I would-n't
Am7
Em
D
Em7
D/F♯
G
Am7
Em
do, you are ev - 'ry-thing now that I've found you.

Am7
Em
Am7
Em
D
Em7
D/F♯
G
Am7
Em
Am7
Em
My pre - cious re - me - dy, take all my pain a - way,
Am7
Em
D
Em7
D/F♯
G
I feel this che - mis - try lov - in' on you.
Am7
Em
Am7
Em
You've switched my world a - round, I feel this way,

Am7
Em
D
Em7
D/F♯
G
my feet don't touch the ground, lov - in' on you.
Am7
Em
Am7
Em
You're so ev - er so high, you fill my heart with a
Am7
Em
D
Em7
D/F♯
G
joy, you are ev - 'ry - thing now that I've found
Am7
Em
Am7
Em
you. I just want you to know, there's noth - ing I would-n't

Am7 Em D Em7 D/F♯ G Am7 Em
do, you are ev - 'ry-thing now that I've found you. You're sun - shine,
Am7 Em Am7 Em D Em7 D/F♯ G
you're sun - shine, you're sun - shine shin - ing down on
(You.) (Me.)
Am7 Em Am7 Em Am7 Em
me. Oh, you're sun - shine. Oh, you're sun - shine. Oh, you're sun - shine
(You.) (Me.)
D Em7 D/F♯ G Em D Cmaj7
shin - ing down on me.
(Me.)
mf

Em
D
C
I just feel this way when you're a-round,
Em
D
C
Em
D
hop-ing that you feel the same. Feels so good to be the one who's hold-
C
D
-ing you, oh, you're my sun-shine.

Am7 Em Am7 Em Am7 Em
You're sun - shine, you're sun - shine, you're sun - shine
D Em7 D/F# G Am7 Em Am7 Em
shin - ing down on me. You're sun - shine, oh, you're sun - shine,
f
Am7 Em D Em7 D/F# G Am7 Em
oh, you're sun - shine shin - ing down on me. You're sun - shine,
Am7 Em Am7 Em D Em7 D/F# G
you're sun - shine, you're sun - shine shin - ing down on.
(You.) (Me.)

Am7
Em
Am7
Em
Am7
Em
You're so ev - er so high, you fill my heart with a joy, you are ev - 'ry-thing
D
Em7
D/F#
G
Am7
Em
Am7
Em
Am7
Em
now that I've found you.
(You.)
(Me.)
D
Em7
D/F#
G
Em
D
Cmaj7
Shin - ing down on me.
mf

Tilted

Words & Music by Gabriel Stebbing & Heloise Letissier

C C/E G5 C C/E
3fr
- 'ry morn-ing with eyes all red, I'll miss___ them for all the tears they shed.
___ them with my eu - pho - ri - a, when they___ said 'Je suis plus folle que toi.'
G5 C C/E G5
But I'm ac - tual - ly good, can't help___ it if we're tilt - ed, I am
C C/E G5 C C/E
ac - tual - ly good, can't help___ it if we,_______ I am ac - tual - ly good, can't help_
G5 C C/E G5
___ it if we're tilt - ed, I am ac - tual - ly good, can't help___ it if we're tilt - ed.________

1.
C
C/E
G5
3fr
C
C/E
G5
3fr
C
C/E
G5
3fr
C
C/E
G5
3fr
2. I miss -
2.
N.C.
(Spoken) Nous et la man on est de sor - tie, pire qu'une sim-ple moi-tié on comp-te à de-mi-de-mi,
(Synth. percussive pad)
mp
pi - le sure un des bas cô-tes com-me des or - i - ga-mis, le bras ten-du pa-raît cas-sé tout n'est qu'é-pis et éc- lis.

Ces en - fants biz - arres, crach - és de - hors comme par has - ard, ca - chant l'ef - fort dans le grif - foir, et
mf
(Drums)
C
G5
3fr
une creep - y song en ét - en - dard qui fait: I'm do - ing my face with ma - gic mark - er,
C
G5
C
I'm in my right place, don't be a down - er. I'm do - ing my face
G5
C
C/E
G5
with ma - gic mark - er, I'm in my right place, don't be a down - er.
I am

C
C/E
G5
3fr
(Vocal ad lib. on repeat)
ac - tual - ly good, can't help it if we're tilt - ed, I am ac - tual - ly good, can't help
it if we, I am ac - tual - ly good, can't help it if we're tilt - ed, I'm good...
Fou, fou, fou, fou. I am ac - tual - ly good, can't help
it if we're tilt - ed,
G5/C
Play 4 times
(Drums)

Trouble

Words by Deborah Carter & Frans Vollink
Music by Frans Vollink

Amaj7
Bmaj7
Emaj7
C♯m7
4fr
f
Oh, I'm fac - ing the bot - tle, oh, for all of my pro - blems. Oh, these In - sta - gram mo - dels, oh, are noth - ing but trou - ble. Oh, I'm fac - ing the bot - tle, oh, for all of my prob - lems.

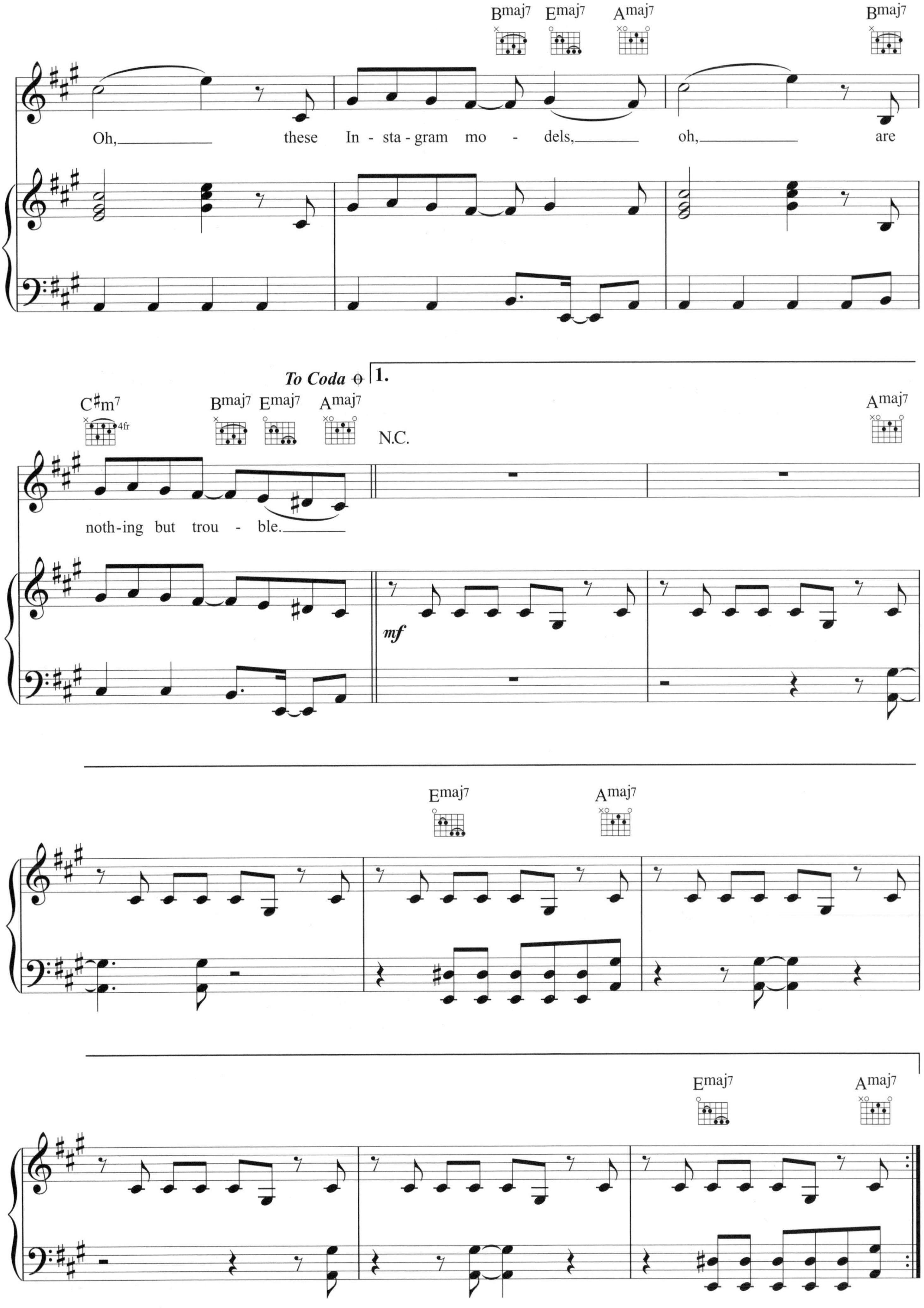

Bmaj7 Emaj7 Amaj7 Bmaj7

Oh, these In - sta - gram mo - dels, oh, are

To Coda 𝄌 1.

C♯m7 Bmaj7 Emaj7 Amaj7 N.C. Amaj7

noth-ing but trou - ble.

mf

Emaj7 Amaj7

Emaj7 Amaj7

2.
Amaj7
Bmaj7
Emaj7
Amaj7
Bmaj7
Emaj7
Amaj7
mp
D.S. al Coda
Bmaj7
Emaj7
Amaj7
Bmaj7
C♯m7
4fr
Bmaj7
Emaj7
Amaj7
Coda
N.C.
mf
Amaj7
Emaj7
Amaj7
Emaj7
Amaj7

Amaj7
Bmaj7
Emaj7
Amaj7
Oh, I'm fac - ing the bot - tle, oh, for
f

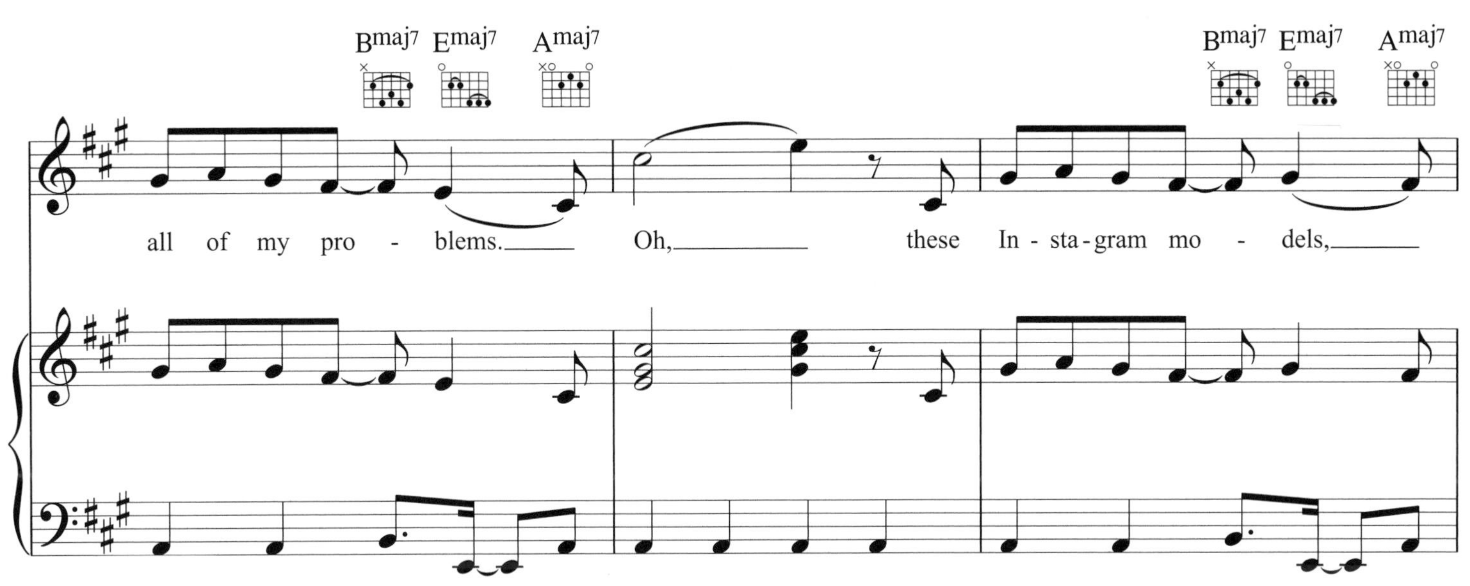
Bmaj7
Emaj7
Amaj7
Bmaj7
Emaj7
Amaj7
all of my pro - blems. Oh, these In - sta - gram mo - dels,

Bmaj7
Amaj7
Bmaj7
Emaj7
Amaj7
oh, are noth - ing but trou - ble.

1 2 3 4 5 6 7 8 9

ALSO AVAILABLE ONLINE AND FROM ALL GOOD MUSIC SHOPS...

Adele: 25
ORDER NO. AM1009712

Adele: The Complete Collection
ORDER NO. AM1011802

Coldplay: A Head Full Of Dreams
ORDER NO. AM1011516

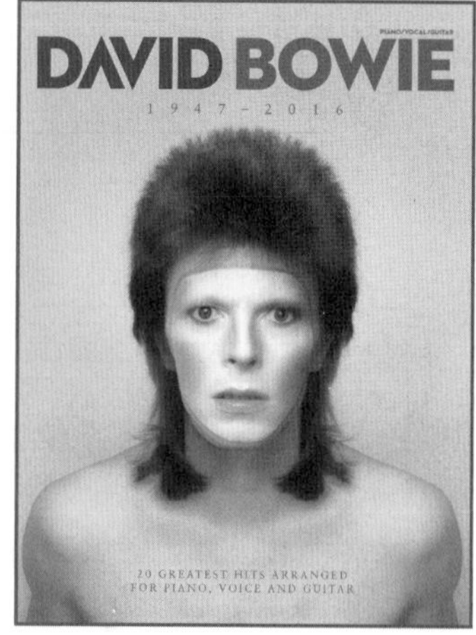

David Bowie 1947 - 2016
ORDER NO. AM1011670

Hits Of The Year 2016
ORDER NO. AM1012330

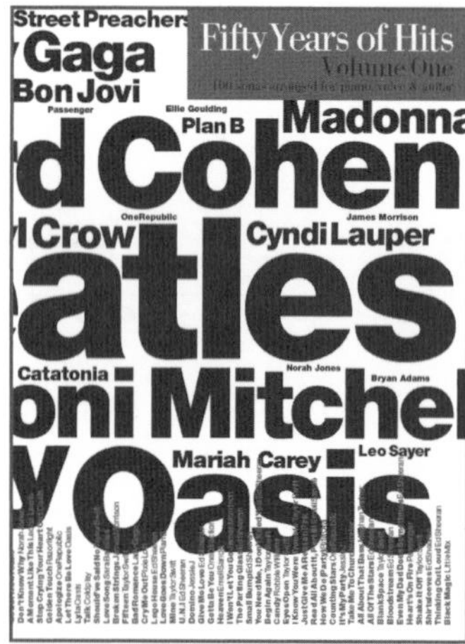

Fifty Years Of Hits: Volume One
ORDER NO. AM1012143

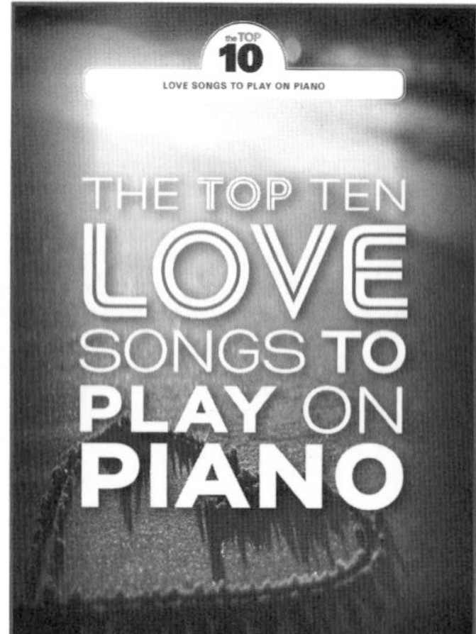

The Top Ten Love Songs To Play On Piano

ORDER NO. AM1012275

The Top Ten Piano Songs Of All Time
ORDER NO. AM1012242

The Top Ten Christmas Songs To Play On Piano
ORDER NO. AM1012484

Really Easy Piano: Chart Hits Vol.3 (Autumn/Winter 2016)
ORDER NO. AM1012033

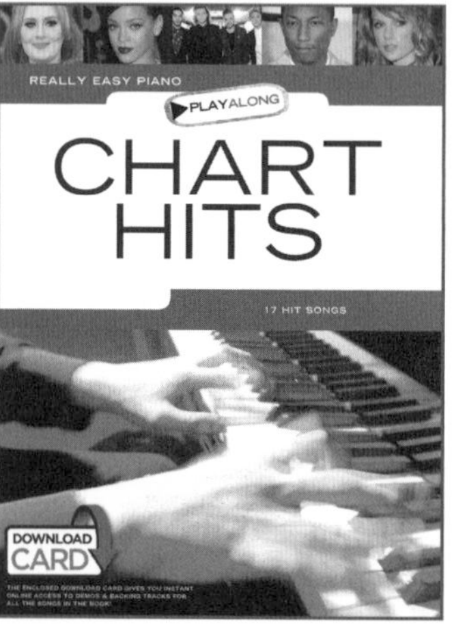

Really Easy Piano Playalong: Chart Hits
ORDER NO. AM1010647

Really Easy Piano: Justin Bieber
ORDER NO. HLE90004893

LOOK OUT FOR MORE TITLES IN THE NOW! MUSIC RANGE

Just visit your local music shop and ask to see our huge range of music in print.
www.musicsales.com